Oxford Physics Series

General Editors

E. J. Burge   D. J. E. Ingram   J. A. D. Matthew

Oxford Physics Series

D. J. E. INGRAM

PROFESSOR OF PHYSICS, UNIVERSITY OF KEELE

Radiation and quantum physics

Clarendon Press · Oxford · 1973

PHYSICS

Oxford University Press, Ely House, London W.1

GLASGOW NEW YORK TORONTO MELBOURNE WELLINGTON
CAPE TOWN IBADAN NAIROBI DAR ES SALAAM LUSAKA ADDIS ABABA
DELHI BOMBAY CALCUTTA MADRAS KARACHI LAHORE DACCA
KUALA LUMPUR SINGAPORE HONG KONG TOKYO

PRINTED IN GREAT BRITAIN BY
J. W. ARROWSMITH LTD., BRISTOL, ENGLAND

Editor's foreword

THE Oxford Physics Series is designed to provide a number of brief texts on topics that cover the whole range of undergraduate physics. This volume relates closely to two other first-year books, *Atoms and their structure* and *Interactions of particles*. Other introductory titles in the series are *d.c. and a.c. circuits*, *Electromagnetism*, and *Atoms in contact*.

As Professor Ingram explains in his first chapter, the title *Radiation and quantum physics* has been carefully chosen to emphasize the link between the development of our understanding of radiation and advances in relation to quantum effects in other fields of physics. The treatment begins by relating a variety of relevant concepts to the everyday phenomena of the production and detection of electromagnetic radiation in its different forms and this conjunction of the familiar and the new material characterizes the whole book.

It is necessary in the restricted length of the text to discriminate between the several aspects of the subject. More important topics, for example the introduction of the Planck constant, and the importance of Young's double-slit experiment, are treated with more attention and with special emphasis on the concepts and understanding involved. On the other hand, experimental details and theoretical complications are mentioned only as words of caution or, on occasions, within the problems at the ends of the chapters. Topics that are more fully considered in other texts of this series, particularly in Professor Conn's *Atoms and their structure*, are dealt with at a level determined by the development of the subject matter, and cross references are provided.

The final chapter links the body of the text to a variety of important ideas, phenomena, and applications. These include the principles of coherence and the laser, detectors of individual quanta, the Mossbauer effect, microwave spectroscopy, and magnetic resonance. Further study within these fields is thus put into perspective and the relevance of what has gone before is made evident. Indeed in nuclear magnetic resonance the quantized nature of radio waves is exhibited and exploited—a fitting complement to the theory of Maxwell, and the experiments of Hertz, with which the book began.

E. J. B.

Preface

INTEGRATION between the different topics and texts is one of the main aims of the Oxford Physics Series—and this book also aims to present an integrated view of its subject in as many ways as possible. The integration is in fact attempted in two ways, first as to level of treatment, and secondly as to subject matter itself. Thus the level is aimed at the interface between school and University to help those in this particular transitional period. Some of the topics treated should already have been met briefly in the last years at school, but this text attempts to take them on from the point of such brief acquaintance to a level that is more appropriate to first-year study at a University. It is hoped that this treatment may make the first stages of University study more understandable, and hence the book may be of equal value in the final stages at school and the first stages at University.

An integration of the subject matter is also attempted throughout the text in a variety of ways. Thus the electromagnetic spectrum is first presented as a whole and the way in which each region relates to it is then discussed. The interplay between advances in our knowledge of radiation and advances in our knowledge of the structure of matter is also maintained throughout the text, since this is a true reflection of the way in which physics itself has progressed. The application of the initial ideas on quantized energy, resulting from Planck and Einstein's work on radiation, is thus followed through to the quantized energy levels within the atom itself. In the same way the particle-like nature of radiation, demonstrated by Compton's work leads on to the wave-like nature of particles. This, in turn, leads on to a consideration of the duality of waves and particles as representing energy and matter, and an introduction to wave-mechanics which justifies the ad hoc quantum postulates of the earlier theories.

This integration can, of course, be extended beyond the realms of physics, since both radiation and its properties, and quantum concepts, are finding increasing importance in chemistry, biology, and the other sciences. It is in fact the author's hope that the approach in this text might also be useful to those studying in these other fields, who would like an introduction to the aspects of physics with which they are likely to be most concerned.

D. J. E. INGRAM

Keele
April 1973

Contents

THE ELECTROMAGNETIC SPECTRUM

Systems involved	Nuclear	Inner electron	Outer electron	Molecular and solid-state	Electrons and nuclei interacting with external fields
Wavelength (metres)	10^{-14}	10^{-10}	10^{-6}	10^{-2}	10^{2}
	γ-rays	X-rays	U.V. Visible Infrared	Microwaves	Radio-waves
Energy (eV)	10^9 10^7	10^5 10^3	10	10^{-1} 10^{-3}	10^{-5} 10^{-7}
Experimental apparatus	Isotopes / Accelerators / Counters	X-ray tubes / Photographic plates	Quartz lens systems / Photocells	Reflection gratings / Radar techniques	Radio-circuits / Valves and transistors

Prisms, gratings, human eye, photographic plates.

1. Radiation and its different forms

The historical setting

AN understanding of the nature of matter and energy has been one of the great challenges to the minds of scientific men ever since any systematic study of the physical world began. The sun was an obvious source of energy to men of the earliest civilizations, and so it is not surprising that radiation in the form of light and heat absorbed their interest as soon as any philosophical or scientific thought was born, as may be found in the writings of many of the ancient civilizations.

In much more recent times the study of radiation, and the different forms it can take, has also paralleled developments in other spheres, and it mirrors, in quite a remarkable way, the history of developing ideas in physics itself. Thus the discovery of new regions of the spectrum, and a deeper understanding of the interactions associated with these different types of radiation, has always gone hand-in-hand with theories on the nature of matter itself, and the different forces and interactions which are associated with it. This continuous link and interplay between the development of our understanding of radiation in its different forms and advances in other fields is not, of course, surprising, since radiation itself is nearly always studied in relation to its interaction with matter. It is for this reason that the title of this book is *Radiation and quantum physics*, rather than just *Radiation* on its own.

This continuous interplay can be followed in a very straightforward historical way, by starting at the centre of the electromagnetic spectrum—in the visible region—and then working out from this in each direction. Thus the first arguments about the nature of radiation were concerned with the nature of light itself, since this particular band of wavelengths can be detected by the human eye without any intervening experimental equipment. Long before the advent of quantum physics, detailed considerations on the nature of light were taking place, and it is interesting to note that even when classical physics reigned supreme there was no complete agreement on whether this radiation had a wave or particle-like nature.

The first moves towards a detailed understanding of the nature of light came with the theoretical studies of Maxwell and the experiments of Hertz. Maxwell was able to correlate the different laws relating to the motion of electric charge, and to show that the electric and magnetic fields which are produced by such accelerating charges would constitute a wave of electromagnetic energy with all the properties of transmission, reflection, and refraction that had been observed for light rays.

2 Radiation and its different forms

The way in which Maxwell was able to derive this very precise and elegant theory is considered in more detail in Chapter 2, but it may be noted that the experimental proof that Maxwell's theory was correct, and applied not only to light waves but also to those of much longer wavelength, came with the experiments of Hertz. He was able to produce the first radio waves from oscillating electric circuits and to detect directly the passage of the associated changing patterns of electric and magnetic fields as they passed across the room from his transmitting to his receiving apparatus.

In this way it became firmly established that these types of radiation were to be associated with the motion of electrical charges, whether they were atomic or subatomic particles in the case of the short wavelengths of visible radiation, or large groups of charge as the current pulses driving a radio-transmitting aerial. The oscillating electric and magnetic fields associated with these moving charges could then be visualized as continuous wave-trains moving out into space and carrying energy with them.

However, experimental results began to accumulate which could not be explained entirely in terms of these continuous wave-trains of electromagnetic fields, such as the discovery of discrete spectral lines in the latter half of the last century. The first explanations of these involved an application of the new concepts of quantized energy. This introduced a new age into theoretical physics and set the background for a deeper understanding of other types of radiation which had been found to exist on both sides of the visible region.

The association of different types of radiation with quanta of different energy was then taken up throughout the various regions of the electromagnetic spectrum, and these different energy changes were then, in turn, linked with the various forces and interactions which produced them. A diagrammatic summary of the different regions of the complete electromagnetic spectrum, together with both the methods used in investigating them, and the kind of information that is obtained from them, is shown at the front. Each of these different regions will now be considered in some detail.

The visible region and its basic properties

The actual range of the visible region is of course determined by the sensitivity of the human eye. This is at a maximum in the yellow part of the spectrum, at a wavelength of approximately 550 nanometres (5.5×10^{-7} m). The sensitivity drops fairly rapidly on either side of this maximum, to die away completely in the violet region, on the one hand, at a wavelength of approximately 400 nanometres (4×10^{-7} m), and in the far red region, on the other hand, at a wavelength of approximately 700 nanometres (7×10^{-7} m). (Such a wavelength is not so difficult to imagine—there are 1 000 millimetres in a metre and about 2 000 wavelengths in a millimetre.) Although this range may appear to be somewhat arbitrarily determined by the subjectivity of human vision, it must be remembered that this depends on the actual mechanism within the human eye for detection of such radiation. This in its turn is determined by the electronic energy levels in the atoms and molecules composing the active material of the eye's retina, and hence, in the end, the range of the visible region is determined by a fairly well defined set of electronic energy levels. It will be seen of course, that the converse of this accounts for the actual production of radiation in the visible region.

Newton was the first to demonstrate unequivocally that white light could be artificially broken up into its separate components by simply passing it through a glass prism. His experiment, forming in this way the first optical spectrum from sunlight, can be considered as the birth of the systematic study of radiation and its properties. His contributions to the study and understanding of the nature of light were of immense significance and his experiments on interference, such as the classic experiment on 'Newton's Rings', produced one of the simplest and most direct methods of measuring the wavelength of these radiations. Nevertheless Newton himself favoured a 'particle' or 'corpuscular' theory of light, and the arguments of the wave theory versus particle theory, initiated at this time, were to continue until they merged into the general considerations of the duality of both matter and energy in terms of waves and particles.

Fig. 1.1 summarizes the main features of the visible region of the spectrum in a symbolic way. Other regions are represented in a similar way in following

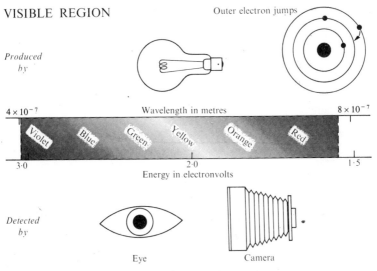

VISIBLE REGION

Outer electron jumps

Produced by

4×10^{-7} Wavelength in metres 8×10^{-7}

Violet   Blue   Green   Yellow   Orange   Red

3·0   2·0   1·5

Energy in electronvolts

Detected by

Eye   Camera

FIG. 1.1.

figures in this chapter. The range of wavelengths, with their associated colours, are shown at the centre of this figure, while the source of radiation is indicated at the top, and the methods of detecting it are indicated at the bottom. The normal method of producing the radiation in practice is shown at the top left hand side, and, in this case of visible radiation, is represented by a simple tungsten electric lamp. The ultimate source of the radiation is indicated—on the top right hand side—as electron jumps between the energy levels of the atoms in the solid tungsten which forms the filament wire of the lamp. This essential characterization of the visible region, as associated with the electron jumps in the outer orbitals of the atom, was not understood, of course, until well after Newton's time.

It will be seen that another set of numbers is also shown across the centre band of Fig. 1.1. These represent the energies associated with the particular wavelengths, measured in electronvolts. This energy is related to the frequency of the radiation by Planck's quantum postulate, $E = h\nu$, as discussed in detail in the next chapter. The frequency and wavelength are also related by the fact that their product is equal to the velocity of light. Hence the energy of the radiation will be directly proportional to both the frequency, ν, and the wavenumber (i.e. the number of wavelengths in unit distance, equal to $1/\lambda$). These parameters are therefore often used to characterize the radiation. They are related by the equations

$$\text{Energy} = h\nu = hc/\lambda \qquad (1.1)$$

where h is the Planck constant and equal to $6{\cdot}626 \times 10^{-34}$ joule second and c is the velocity of light and equal to $2{\cdot}998 \times 10^8$ m s^{-1}. The standard unit for energy in the internationally agreed system is the joule, but in the study of spectra the unit of the electronvolt, or the associated frequency, or wavenumber, is often more convenient. The electronvolt is the energy acquired by one electron in falling through a potential-energy difference of one volt. It can thus be easily visualized, as it measures the electron jumps directly. Since the energy differences between the outer orbits of atoms are of the order of a few volts, it follows that the energy changes giving rise to radiation in the visible region will be of the order of a few electronvolts, as indicated in Fig. 1.1. It should be pointed out, however, that the actual amount of energy associated with one electronvolt is extremely small, since it only measures the energy associated with one single electron. The conversion from joules to electronvolts is given by

$$1 \text{ joule} = 6{\cdot}24 \times 10^{18} \text{ electronvolts}$$

or

$$1 \text{ eV} = 1{\cdot}60 \times 10^{-19} \text{ J}, \qquad (1.2)$$

and the wavenumber is related to the energy in electronvolts by the equation

$$h\nu \text{ (in eV)} = (1/\lambda) \, 1{\cdot}243 \times 10^{-6} \qquad (1.3)$$

where λ is measured in metres.

Also summarized in Fig. 1.1 are the practical methods whereby the radiation can be detected. In this particular region the human eye itself does of course form the main method of detection. More permanent methods are represented by the camera and the photographic plate.

The ultraviolet region and its properties

Simple experiments, in which a photographic plate is held behind the visible spectrum as displayed in Fig. 1.1, indicate directly that, although the human eye ceases to be sensitive to radiation beyond the violet end of the visible colour range, there is nevertheless radiation which does extend beyond this region, and which can fog the photographic plate. This can also be shown to be true at the other end of the spectrum. A photographic plate suitably sensitized can be shown to be fogged well out beyond the red end of the spectrum, and a sensitive thermometer or thermopile will indicate that energy is falling on it.

Turning first to the shorter-wavelength, higher-energy region, we go beyond the violet and into the ultraviolet. The main properties of this region are briefly characterized in Fig. 1.2, in the same way as they have been previously characterized for the visible region in Fig. 1.1.

Although ultraviolet radiation is invisible to the human eye, its existence can be simply and strikingly demonstrated by letting the radiation from a discharge tube fall on a fluorescent screen. The ultraviolet radiation is absorbed by atoms in the fluorescent material and produces energy changes within them. Some of these give rise to energy jumps which are smaller than those associated with the incoming radiation. As a result of such electron jumps, visible radiation is emitted which can be detected by the human eye. This conversion of the higher-energy, shorter-wavelength ultraviolet radiation to the lower-energy, longer-wavelength visible light is the essential feature of such phenomena as fluorescence, and is, of course, used in a very practical way in fluorescent poster paints. These, and other similar devices, absorb the ultraviolet radiation falling on to the poster and then re-emit this in a particular range of the visible region, adding to the visible light which is also being reflected.

This process of detecting ultraviolet radiation is illustrated schematically in Fig. 1.2 together with some more quantitative methods. These include photoelectric cells, where individual quanta of the incoming ultraviolet radiation can cause electrons to be emitted from a metal surface. The electrons can then be counted by electronic means. As mentioned previously, it is also possible to detect the ultraviolet radiation by means of a photographic plate, provided a quartz or other suitable lens system is used in the associated camera, since glass lenses are opaque to most ultraviolet wavelengths.

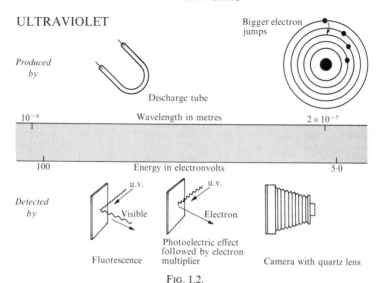

FIG. 1.2.

As in the case of the visible region, the source of the ultraviolet radiation is indicated at the top of Fig. 1.2 and is represented by a gas discharge tube, which is basically similar to the neon or fluorescent tubes so common in everyday life. In such a tube the electrical discharge excites the electrons in the atoms which then fall back to the ground state, emitting ultraviolet radiation in the process. The actual nature and wavelength of the emitted radiation will depend on the particular atoms and gases contained within the tube, and for the greatest efficiency of production of ultraviolet radiation, atoms such as mercury are often used. It will be appreciated that the ultimate source of this ultraviolet radiation is therefore once again the electron jumps within the orbitals of the atoms concerned. The mechanism is thus still basically the same as in the visible region. However, since ultraviolet radiation is more energetic than visible light, the energy associated with the electron jumps must be greater. Therefore these electron jumps may well be across two or more energy levels rather than between the outermost levels as is the case for the visible region. These somewhat larger electron jumps are indicated schematically on the top right-hand side of Fig. 1.2, for comparison with a similar representation in Fig. 1.1.

The quantitative characteristics of this region of the spectrum are summarized across the centre of Fig. 1.2 where the wavelength range is shown as extending from 2×10^{-7} to 10^{-8} m, and the associated energies are also given. These extend from about 5 electronvolts, bordering on the visible region, to 100 electronvolts, at the higher-energy end. It will be appreciated that none of these regions of the spectrum begins or ends precisely at any given wavelength, or energy value, and there is in fact a continuous overlap between all the different regions.

The X-ray region

In considering the visible and ultraviolet regions, attention has been concentrated on the outer electrons of the atoms concerned, and the jumps between the outer orbits. The question may very well be raised, however, as to the type of radiation which will be produced if the inner electrons of large atoms are disturbed. Large atoms have many electrons in orbits around the nucleus. The large nuclear charge produces deep energies for the inner orbits (i.e. a great deal of work is required to remove the electron from such orbits). If an electron is removed from one of these inner orbits, one of the outer electrons may fall right across many electron orbitals to the empty inner site. This will produce a very large energy change, and so radiation will be emitted which is much more energetic than that associated with the outer orbits alone. This highly energetic electron transition is, in fact, the origin of the highly energetic and penetrating X-ray emission lines.

In a normal X-ray tube electrons are first accelerated through a high voltage V, and then hit a heavy-metal anode where they are very rapidly retarded. This rapid deceleration of electric charge will produce electromagnetic radiation, and the maximum frequency of this is determined by the relation

$$h\nu_{max} = \text{maximum kinetic-energy loss} = eV. \tag{1.4}$$

More detailed consideration of the way in which these processes actually give rise to X-rays will be found in Chapter 6.

The general properties of the X-ray region spectrum can, therefore, be summarized briefly as in Fig. 1.3. The source of spectral emission lines in this region is now seen to be the highly energetic electron jump, right across all the orbitals associated with a large heavy atom. The way in which this can be produced in practice is indicated schematically on the left-hand side, as usual, where the beam of fast electrons, moving within an evacuated tube, is allowed to fall on a heavy metal, such as copper or tungsten, to produce the X-radiation. The methods of detecting such radiation are indicated at the bottom of the figure. As in the last two regions, it is possible to use a photographic plate—a fact well known in medical science. This particular application of X-radiation, to penetrate less dense material and reveal internal structure, was followed up very quickly by their initial discoverer, and still remains one of the main fields of application.

The wavelengths have now shortened so that over 10^{10} can be included within the space of one metre, while the energies of the photons corresponding to the higher end of this wavelength region, have now risen to about 10^5 electronvolts. This photon energy range, from one electronvolt in the visible

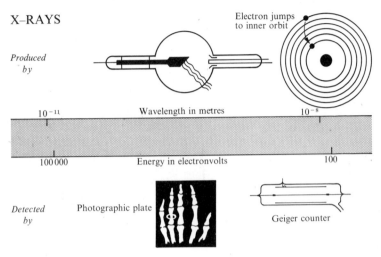

FIG. 1.3.

region to just on 100 000 electronvolts in the X-ray region, indicates the very wide range of energies associated with the electronic levels of atoms. Thus radiation in all three different regions of spectrum, the visible, ultraviolet, and X-ray, can arise from electron jumps within these atomic orbitals.

If energy changes within the total range of electronic energy levels have now been exhausted, the question arises whether it is possible to produce radiation of still higher energy. However, fairly soon after the discovery of X-rays, it was discovered that higher-energy radiation with characteristic wavelengths, indicating transitions between specific energy levels, did exist, and could be detected from radioactive nuclei. The existence of this higher-energy radiation, known as γ-rays, must therefore imply the existence of other deeper-seated energy-level systems, and studies of these systems led on to the investigations of γ-ray spectroscopy, and the forces and interactions associated with this.

γ-Radiation and the nucleus

An energy-level system which produces energy changes much larger than those associated with the electronic structure of the atom, must involve forces and interactions which are much stronger than those between the electrons and the nucleus. The realization that these highly energetic γ-rays must come from *within* the nucleus suggested that they could be used to characterize the energy levels within various nuclei, and hence probe the forces and interactions inside them. The sources of such high-energy γ-ray spectral lines are represented schematically in Fig. 1.4.

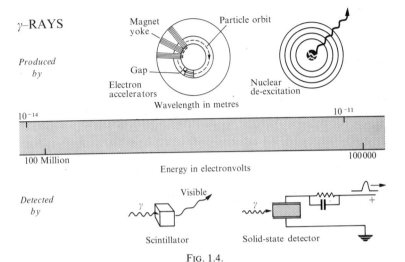

FIG. 1.4.

To produce such nuclear energy changes we need radioactive isotopes or the use of high-energy particle accelerators. In such particle accelerators protons, for example, are accelerated to very high energies and then projected at various different nuclei so that excited energy states are produced within them. The γ-ray spectral lines are then emitted when the nucleus reverts from its excited state to its ground state, i.e. the state of lowest energy. The deceleration of the very fast electrons from such an accelerator produces electromagnetic radiation in exactly the same way as X-rays, but the higher energies involved now give rise to the higher-frequency γ-rays. The γ-radiation is normally detected by specially constructed counters, which often rely on the scintillation effects produced by the incoming γ-rays. The emitted light quanta can be detected by photoelectric cells and amplified and recorded electronically.

The wavelengths and the energies associated with this end of the spectrum are indicated across the centre of Fig. 1.4, and at the higher-energy end these reach into the thousand-million-electronvolt region. Although there may be an upper limit to the energy changes which can be associated with any given nucleus, it is possible to produce still higher-energy radiation from the annihilation of matter and anti-matter, or by the acceleration of charged particles in outer space, and hence there is really no upper limit to this region of the spectrum. At the lower-energy end there is in fact a considerable overlap with the higher-energy end of the X-ray region. In this particular case the overlap is a real and genuine one, since the X-ray region can be defined precisely as radiation arising from electronic energy changes, whereas the γ-ray region, on the other hand, is essentially involved with nuclear energy changes, and not with any energy changes in the electronic structure of the atom.

The infrared region and molecular structure

We have followed the range of wavelengths out to the high-energy end of the electromagnetic spectrum. It is now necessary to return through the visible region and to consider how the total spectrum extends in the opposite direction, to longer wavelengths and lower energies. The first region beyond the visible in this direction is that beyond the red, i.e. the infrared region. The association of this region with thermal radiation has been appreciated for some considerable time. The fact that an electric fire will give out simultaneously both visible radiation, concentrated in the red end, and heat radiation which can be felt but not seen, is a practical demonstration of this association.

The energy changes which correspond to quanta in this region are significantly smaller than the outer electron changes associated with the visible region, and arise from interactions within the molecule or solid lattice as a whole. If the infrared radiation emitted from excited gas molecules is studied, the observed spectral lines can be correlated with the energies of the whole molecule as it vibrates, bends, or undergoes other types of molecular motion. From such studies deductions can be made about the interatomic forces which bind the molecule together. In the infrared radiation emitted from solids the discrete spectral lines are spread out into energy bands, but the measurement of gaps between these can often give precise information about the structure of the crystal lattice.

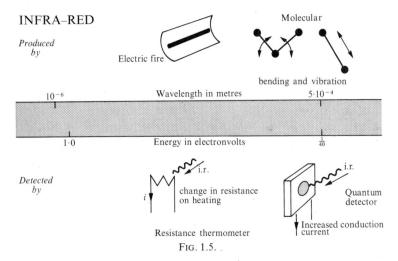

FIG. 1.5.

The case of gaseous spectra is illustrated schematically in the top right hand corner of Fig. 1.5, where the vibrations of a water molecule H_2O are indicated. This triangular molecule has two arms, with a hydrogen atom at each end. The molecule can be either in a state of rapid vibration or in a state of slower vibration, and the energy changes between these two different states of vibration correspond to the energy associated with the emission or absorption of infrared radiation. Different vibrational changes such as this in different molecules will thus give rise to a whole range of infrared wavelengths, and the energies covered by such a range are indicated across the centre of the diagram in the usual way. It can be seen here that the energy changes associated with such molecular motion have now fallen to about one hundredth of the energy changes associated with electronic jumps within the atom, and the wavelength has correspondingly risen to a value of about 10^{-4} m.

The microwave region and its applications

As the wavelength of the radiation becomes longer, so the infrared radiation, or heat region of the spectrum, merges into the microwave region. Here the discrete spectral lines are still to be associated with molecular motion, but the normal sensation of heat waves is no longer felt. This region of the spectrum is of some historical interest, since there was in fact a gap across this wavelength band, which was only closed by the war-time research on radar during the 1940s. Before that date the infrared region had been fairly well investigated, and radio-waves had, of course, been used for some decades. The advent of suitable sources of radiation in the microwave, or centimetre-wavelength band, awaited the development of radar, however, and the closing of this gap in the electromagnetic spectrum was thus not only of great practical value but also produced the complete integrated spectrum for the first time.

As mentioned above, the source of quantized radiation in this region is still the motion of the molecules as a whole, but the energy changes are now smaller than the vibrational motion associated with the infrared region. The motion that gives rise to microwave radiation is associated with the tumbling or rotation of molecules, or the inversion, or 'turning inside out', of such molecules as ammonia. This is indicated in the right hand corner of Fig. 1.6. The ammonia molecule is shown as a pyramid with a nitrogen atom at the top, above a plane formed by the three hydrogen atoms. This nitrogen atom can exist equally well above or below the plane formed by the hydrogen atoms, and does in fact oscillate between these two positions, inverting the molecule as it does so. The frequency of this molecular inversion is in fact 24 000 MHz, and corresponds to a wavelength of 1·25 cm. It is thus noticeably longer than the waves in the infrared region of the spectrum, and falls in the middle of the microwave region.

The practical ways in which such radiation can be produced, however, are

MICROWAVE REGION

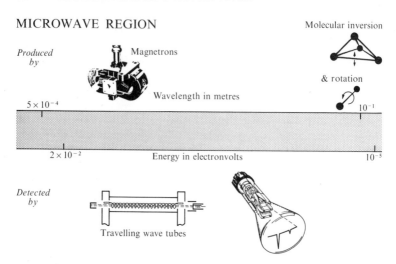

FIG. 1.6.

very different from the thermal means indicated for the last region, and a much more precise control of power generation, and wavelength of operation, can be effected by electronic means. In fact all the precise electronic methods were extended from the radio-wavelengths into the microwave region to produce radar valves known as the magnetron and klystron. These valves can produce monochromatic radiation in which all the power is concentrated in a very narrow range of wavelengths. In the same way, radiation in this region of the spectrum is detected by electronic methods, as illustrated by the travelling wave tube drawn at the bottom of Fig. 1.6. It will be seen that the techniques applicable to this region of the spectrum are entirely different from those used for shorter wavelengths. The wavelengths in the microwave region are of such a magnitude that they can be measured by ordinary centimetre rules, and hence diffraction and interference experiments can be set up on this region of the spectrum with gratings made from simple wire lattices. Demonstrations of the basic properties of electromagnetic radiation can thus be carried out very easily with microwaves.

The radio-region of the spectrum

Moving from the microwave region to still longer wavelengths brings us into the radio region of the spectrum, where the wavelengths of the electromagnetic radiation can reach to hundreds, or thousands, of metres. This region of the spectrum was first investigated and exploited by such people as Hertz, Maxwell, and Marconi, and the advent of radio-waves had, of course, an enormous impact not only on a basic scientific understanding of the nature of electromagnetic radiation, but also on the whole field of communications. The fact that it was easier to produce radiation at these longer wavelengths than in the microwave region is due to the limited speed at which electrons move across an amplifying device. Thus if they can traverse the active part of the device in a time short compared with one period of the oscillation, efficient amplification occurs, but at the higher frequencies they become out of phase with each other, and amplification is not obtained. The long waves of the radio-region were therefore ideal for experimentation, and rapid development of all the electronic methods of controlling and amplifying them soon followed. These practical methods of producing and detecting them are illustrated symbolically in Fig. 1.7. These involve tuned circuits with lumped constants,

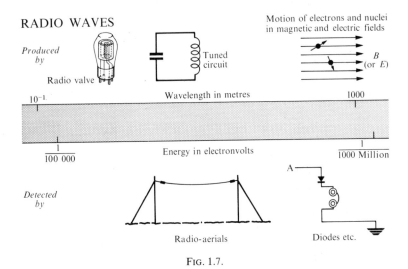

FIG. 1.7.

such as individual capacitors and inductances, and the wavelength of the resulting oscillations is simply determined by adjusting the magnitude of these different parameters. In the same way, detection was effected by a simple aerial system with a silicon crystal, or other detecting device, which could filter off the modulation from the carrier waves and display the information carried by the modulated signal.

The integrated spectrum

In the previous sections the different features of the various regions of the electromagnetic spectrum have been briefly summarized, and in particular the different forces and interactions that give rise to the various energy changes have been considered. Although these vary considerably in their nature and magnitude, as do the ways of producing and detecting the radiation in the different regions, it should nevertheless be stressed that the actual electromagnetic radiation itself has the same fundamental properties in wha.ever region of the spectrum it is to be found.

The basic electromagnetic nature of radiation gives rise to its general properties of propagation which can be demonstrated readily in quite different regions of the spectrum. Thus the reflection of electromagnetic radiation can be demonstrated in the visible region by a silver mirror and in the microwave region by a sheet of metal or fine wire screen. In both cases it is the interaction of the radiation with the free electrons in the conducting surface which produces the reflection. In the same way, properties like refraction can be demonstrated by glass prisms on the one hand, and paraffin prisms on the other. Moreover, effects which depend on the wavelength can also be demonstrated in quite different regions of the spectrum, and only the scale of the experimental apparatus need be changed. Thus the diffraction and interference patterns produced by a fine-ruled grating in the visible region can be demonstrated very simply in the microwave region by vertical slats of metal spaced a centimetre or so apart.

The quantum nature of the radiation can also be demonstrated in quite different regions of the spectrum, although the size of the quanta varies by many orders of magnitude as one moves from one end of the spectrum to the other. The particle-like nature of radiation becomes more and more pronounced as the value of its energy increases and the momentum associated with the individual quanta then becomes significant. Hence these quantum effects are all readily demonstrated in the higher-energy regions as discussed in detail in Chapter 5.

PROBLEMS

1.1. The visible region of the spectrum is generally considered to spread from a wavelength of 4×10^{-7} m at the violet end, to a wavelength of 7×10^{-7} m at the red end. What is the frequency bandwidth, in Hz (cycles/second), covered by this spread?

1.2. An electron, moving in the outer orbitals of an atom, jumps from one energy state to another with an energy 3·5 eV lower than that of the first. What is the frequency and wavelength of the emitted radiation?

1.3. Ultraviolet light of $9·4 \times 10^{-8}$ m wavelength is absorbed by a hydrogen atom. If its electron was originally in a level lying at a depth of 110 000 cm^{-1} what will be the depth of the level to which it is excited?

1.4. The interatomic spacing between atoms in a crystal is of the order of 5×10^{-10} m. What is the ratio of this distance to the wavelength of an X-ray which has been emitted by an atom in which the electron has undergone an energy-level change of 5 000 eV?

1.5. The nucleus of an atom is bombarded with particles from a high-energy accelerator. If the energy of the bombarding particle is 5 MeV and half of this is absorbed by the nucleus to excite it into a higher state, calculate the wavelength of the emitted γ-ray if the nucleus returns to its ground state by the emission of one such γ-ray.

1.6. Calculate the ratio of the energy changes that occur when an outer electron in an atom changes orbits and emits a wavelength of $6 \cdot 5 \times 10^{-7}$ m, compared with the change in rotational motion of a diatomic molecule which produces an infrared emission line of frequency 9×10^{12} MHz

1.7. A diffraction grating is to be constructed to demonstrate the properties of interference and diffraction with microwave radiation, and the distance between successive slots is to be equal to half the wavelength of the radiation employed. Calculate what this spacing should be if the grating is to be irradiated with microwaves from a magnetron operating at a frequency of 9 000 MHz.

1.8. The rotational energy of a linear molecule is given by the expression

$$E = J(J+1)h^2/8\pi^2 I$$

where J is an integer and I is the moment of inertia of the molecule. Calculate the wavelength of the radiation emitted when the molecule reduces its rotational energy by dropping from the state with $J = 4$ to $J = 3$, if its moment of inertia is equal to $1 \cdot 38 \times 10^{-45}$ kg m^2.

1.9. In what regions of the spectrum will lie (i) the transition corresponding to the $J = 2$ to $J = 1$ energy change of the molecule in Problem 1.8, and (ii) the transition corresponding to the $J = 20$ to $J = 19$ energy change?

1.10. The light from a helium–neon laser is obtained when neon atoms fall from an energy level which has a wavenumber of $1 \cdot 5086 \times 10^7$ m^{-1} to one with a wavenumber of $1 \cdot 3506 \times 10^7$ m^{-1}. What is the wavelength and approximate colour of the laser light which is emitted?

1.11. One of the more important spectral lines studied in the γ-ray region of the spectrum arises from an energy change of 14·4 KeV within the nucleus of an iron atom. What are the frequencies and wavelengths of the spectral line emitted?

1.12. The energy of a small bar magnet of magnetic moment μ in a magnetic field of strength B is given by $\mp\mu.B$, the $\mp$ corresponding to the bar magnet being aligned with or against the field. In experiments on magnetic resonance, electrons of magnetic moment $9 \cdot 27 \times 10^{-24}$ joule/tesla are aligned with and against a magnetic field of 0·3 tesla. Calculate the difference in energy of the two groups, and the wavelength of the radiation that will be emitted when a transition takes place between them.

2. The nature of radiation

Classical and quantum models

IN this chapter all the different regions of the electromagnetic spectrum are considered together, and models and theories are developed which are applicable throughout the whole region. We have already seen that there are basically two types of model, or theory, which can be used to account for the nature and behavior of the electromagnetic radiation, i.e. the classical theory, which interprets the radiation in terms of a continuous wave-motion, and the quantum model, which attributes particle-like properties to the radiation to explain its properties.

The classical wave theory began by considering the radiation as waves moving through a medium which could be described in terms of macroscopic properties and represented by various parameters which took no account of the atomic constitution of the medium. Concepts like dielectric constants, permeability, and refractivity could thus be attributed to the medium as a whole. The propagation and nature of the radiation could be described in these terms without any necessity for a detailed picture of the atomic constitution of the medium. This approach could then be modified by considering the interactions of the electromagnetic waves with such individual entities as free electrons. The additional effects produced by these interactions could then be calculated and incorporated in the same general classical picture of wave-motion in macroscopic terms. Following this, a kind of semi-quantized picture can be developed, in which the energy levels of the atoms or molecular systems that interact with the vibrations of the continuous electromagnetic radiation are taken to be quantized. However further investigation of the detailed mechanism of the interaction of the radiation with the atoms or of the way in which radiation is produced by them, reveals the inadequacy of the purely classical approach. It then becomes necessary to formulate the quantum model of both the radiation and the atoms with which it interacts.

Historically, the first convincing evidence of the quantized nature of the interaction of radiation with matter came from Einstein's application of Planck's concepts to give an explanation of the photoelectric effect; the models of quantized levels associated with the atoms came a little later when Bohr applied these same ideas to atomic structure. The demonstration of the momentum associated with the particle-like nature of radiation at higher energies then came from Compton's experiments on X-ray scattering. Hence the quantum model, and the particle-like nature of radiation, came to be established and accepted.

The way in which Planck introduced the idea of quantized energy, in order to account for the radiation laws, is outlined in this chapter. The next three chapters consider the other crucial experiments which helped to develop ideas on the nature of radiation, the apparent contradiction between the wave and particle theories that followed, and whether any coherent model can be drawn from them.

Maxwell's theory of electromagnetic waves

The first studies on the nature of radiation, and of light in particular, were due to Newton and his contemporaries, such as Huygens who developed the general concept of propagation by wave-motion. Thus Huygens enunciated the fundamental principle to explain wave propagation, and stated that 'every point in a wave-front can be considered as acting as a new source of secondary waves'. This can then be developed to account for rectilinear propagation (i.e. geometrical optics) on the one hand, and diffraction and interference effects on the other. This kind of treatment essentially depends on the geometrical properties of space, however, and no account is taken of the nature of the medium through which the waves are travelling, nor indeed of the actual physical nature of the waves themselves.

The first steps in this direction came from the work of Clerk Maxwell who was able to produce an extremely sophisticated and quantitative theory, relating the propagation of the electromagnetic waves to the properties of the medium through which they travelled. In order to do this, the basic properties of the medium must be related to the changing patterns of electric and magnetic fields of the wave-motion. Maxwell therefore had to summarize and correlate various laws relating to electrostatics and magnetostatics, and express these in such a way that they could be combined to account for the behavior of electromagnetic waves as they pass through the medium. Since Maxwell's theory gave the first detailed picture of electromagnetic waves, a brief summary of the way in which he developed it will now be given. The full mathematical treatment is not appropriate here but may be found in *Electromagnetism* by F. N. H. Robinson (ops 1).

The four basic laws taken by Maxwell were (i) Ampère's Law, defining the magnetic field produced by a current, (ii) Faraday's Law defining the electromotive force produced by a changing magnetic field, (iii) Gauss's Law defining the electric-field intensity in terms of free electric charge in the medium, and (iv) a similar relation for the magnetic-field intensity but with the number of free magnetic poles always equal to zero.

Before correlating and integrating these four relations, Maxwell first had to extend Ampère's law so that it also applied to the case of time-varying currents and fields. Fig. 2.1(a) represents Ampère's law as applied to the static case of a constant current, i, flowing in a wire, with the concentric lines

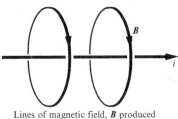

Lines of magnetic field, B produced
by current, or charge flow, i

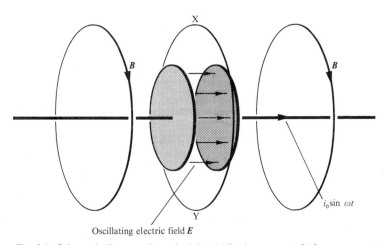

Oscillating electric field E

FIG. 2.1. Schematic diagram of Ampère's law (a) for d.c. currents, (b) for a.c. currents.

of magnetic flux, B, which are associated with it. If two plates of a capacitor
are now included in the circuit, as shown in Fig. 2.1(b), and an a.c. voltage is
applied, there will be an a.c. current flow of magnitude $V(\omega C)$, if all the
impedance is due to the capacitor. Therefore we should expect concentric
lines of oscillating magnetic flux around the wire, as before. Maxwell argued
that these would also continue around the space occupied by the capacitor to
form a continuous flux distribution, but application of the initial form of
Ampère's law which relates magnetic flux around a closed curve to the
current flowing through the area of the curve would predict a zero value when
applied to the particular circular curve XY of Fig. 2.1(b). Maxwell resolved
this paradox by suggesting that, as well as the current formed by the motion
of the electrons along the wire, there existed a 'displacement current' due to
the changing magnitude of the electric field between the plates of the capacitor

as it charged and discharged. The mathematical formulation of this extended version of Ampère's law then becomes

$$\oint_l \boldsymbol{B}.\mathrm{d}\boldsymbol{l} = \mu_0 \boldsymbol{i} + \mu_0 \int_s \varepsilon_0 \frac{\partial \boldsymbol{E}}{\partial t}.\mathrm{d}\boldsymbol{S} \tag{2.1}$$

where the first integral is taken round the closed loop, and μ_0 is the permeability of free space. The second integral, that of the displacement current, is taken over the area of the loop, and ε_0 is the permittivity of free space. There is then a close correlation to the mathematical formulation of Faraday's law, which relates the strength of an induced electric field to the rate of change of magnetic flux, and can be written as

$$\text{Induced e.m.f.} = \oint_l \boldsymbol{E}.\mathrm{d}\boldsymbol{l} = -\int_s \mu_0 \frac{\partial \boldsymbol{H}}{\partial t}.\mathrm{d}\boldsymbol{S} \tag{2.2}$$

and is expressed diagrammatically in Fig. 2.2.

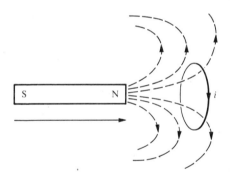

FIG. 2.2. Faraday's law of electromagnetic induction. Changing lines of magnetic flux induce e.m.f. and current in loop of wire.

Gauss's law can be represented schematically by the flux diverging from a quantity of charge, as shown in Fig. 2.3, and can be represented mathematically by the equation

$$\oint_s \boldsymbol{E}.\mathrm{d}\boldsymbol{S} = \oint_V \frac{\rho}{\varepsilon_0} \mathrm{d}V, \tag{2.3}$$

where the first integral is taken over the area of a surface surrounding the charge, and the second integral is the volume integral over all the enclosed charge.

It can also be shown that a similar relation holds for the divergence of a magnetic field, but since isolated magnetic poles cannot exist, the right hand

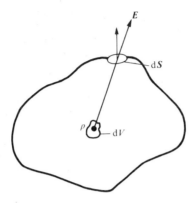

FIG. 2.3. Gauss's law for flux diverging from electric charge. The integral of the field over the surface is equal to the total charge enclosed, divided by ε_0.

side of the equation is now always zero, i.e.

$$\oint_s \boldsymbol{B}.\mathrm{d}\boldsymbol{S} = 0. \tag{2.4}$$

For the propagation through free-space, the value of i and q will be zero, and the four equations reduce to two simple pairs, i.e.

$$\oint_l \boldsymbol{B}\,\mathrm{d}l = \mu_0\varepsilon_0 \int_s \frac{\partial \boldsymbol{E}}{\partial t}.\mathrm{d}\boldsymbol{S} \quad \text{and} \quad \oint_l \boldsymbol{E}.\mathrm{d}l = -\int_s \frac{\partial \boldsymbol{B}}{\partial t}.\mathrm{d}\boldsymbol{S},$$

$$\oint_s \boldsymbol{E}.\mathrm{d}\boldsymbol{S} = 0 \qquad \oint_s \boldsymbol{B}.\mathrm{d}\boldsymbol{S} = 0.$$

Maxwell was able to take these four basic equations and combine them into a single equation relating the form of the magnetic- and electric-field variations in both time and space. Specifically he was able to show they obeyed the fundamental equation for wave motion in three-dimensional space, which can be written as

$$\frac{\partial^2 E_x}{\partial x^2} + \frac{\partial^2 E_x}{\partial y^2} + \frac{\partial^2 E_x}{\partial z^2} - \mu_0\varepsilon_0 \frac{\partial^2 E_x}{\partial t^2} = 0 \tag{2.5}$$

and similarly for the y- and z-components. This is the general equation of a wave moving in three-dimensional space with a velocity given by the square root of the inverse of the coefficient of $-\dfrac{\partial^2 E}{\partial t^2}$

$$\text{i.e.} \quad \text{velocity} = \frac{1}{\sqrt{(\mu_0\varepsilon_0)}}. \tag{2.6}$$

Exactly the same equation can be derived for the variation in B, as for E, and hence Maxwell was able to show that the four basic equations lead to an electromagnetic wave propagation of simultaneous waveforms of E and B, with a velocity equal to $1/\sqrt{(\mu_0\varepsilon_0)}$. Substitution of the experimentally measured values of μ_0 and ε_0 into this expression, moreover, gives good agreement with the measured velocity of light.

Nowadays this calculation is in fact reversed, and the statement that the velocity of light, c, is equal to $(\mu_0\varepsilon_0)^{-\frac{1}{2}}$ is used to calculate the value of ε_0 from the measured value of c, and the value of μ_0 taken by definition as $4\pi \times 10^{-7}$ henry m^{-1}. Maxwell was able to give a very complete explanation of the existence and properties of electromagnetic waves since this simple theory can be readily extended to conducting and anisotropic media, to account for reflection, refraction, and many other observed wave phenomena. This self-consistent classical picture of electromagnetic radiation can be represented for the simplest case of a plane-polarized wave travelling along the z-direction by the oscillating electric and magnetic fields illustrated in Fig. 2.4.

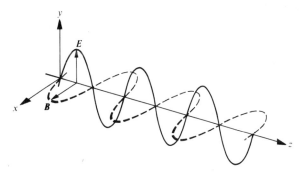

FIG. 2.4. Representation of plane-polarized electromagnetic wave. The E-vector oscillates in the y-direction, the B-vector in the x-direction while the wave propagates along the z-axis.

At the turn of the century, however, various phenomena began to be discovered, which could not be explained by this straightforward classical picture of radiation.

The radiation laws

The particular problem facing Planck, and others of his contemporaries, who were trying to explain and understand the nature of the radiation laws, can be summarized by considering the radiation which is emitted from a 'black body'. The idea of a 'black body' was introduced to represent a perfect absorber and emitter of radiation. The concept of a perfect absorber of radiation is relatively easy to visualize, thus any surface which will absorb completely all types of radiation falling on it, and reflect none in the whole wavelength range, can be thought of as a 'perfect absorber' of radiation, and can be fairly well approximated by a layer of charcoal, or other black matt material. An even better approximation can be obtained by taking a large hollow sphere, and coating the inside of this with such black absorbent material. If a small hole is then drilled in the side of the sphere, any radiation which enters through this hole will either be absorbed completely when it first hits the opposite interior surface, or, if any is reflected from this, it will be absorbed at successive reflection points, as it bounces round inside the sphere. This action of totally absorbing all the incoming radiation that falls on the small hole is represented schematically in Fig. 2.5, and it can be seen that such a simple device as this does produce a more or less perfect absorber of all the wavelength ranges which fall on the small hole in the sphere.

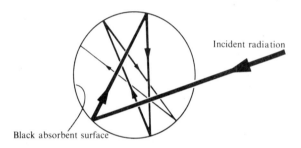

FIG. 2.5. Action of a 'black body'. Radiation incident through the small entry hole is entirely absorbed after successive reflections.

Although it is relatively easy to visualize the concept of the 'perfect absorber', as defined in the last paragraph, the idea of a 'perfect emitter' of radiation would be much harder to conceive, or define, from first principles. Thus it obviously cannot be a body which emits energy equally at all wavelengths since there is nothing to limit the amount of energy so emitted. Instead of considering 'the perfection' of the emission process itself, however, it is quite straightforward to approach this definition from the simple fact that the absorption and emission properties of any surface must be exactly correlated. Thus any surface which is good at absorbing radiation that falls on it, will also be good at emitting radiation, if it is heated above its surroundings; while a surface which is bad at absorbing radiation and reflects most of that falling on it, will also be a poor emitter of radiation. This may be stated in a more quantitative fashion, by saying that the coefficients of emissivity, and of absorptivity, of a given surface must be equal, a fact which can be formally proved thermodynamically by considering the way in which a body reaches equilibrium with its surroundings if suspended in an evacuated enclosure.

It can be seen that it is now possible to define a perfect emitting surface, as being identical to a perfect absorbing surface, rather than having to define what particular energies it will emit under different conditions. Thus, since our black body of Fig. 2.5 will absorb all radiation falling on it, and is thus a perfect absorber, it must now follow that, if this is heated up above its surrounding temperature, the radiation which it emits, i.e. coming out from the small hole in its side, will be that corresponding to a 'perfect emitter'. Moreover it is now possible by experiment to determine the energy distribution with wavelength that will be associated with a 'perfect emitter', i.e. the energy–wavelength distribution of a 'perfect emitter' is that emitted from such a black body when this is raised to any specified temperature.

The energy emitted from such a black body, and the way that this varies with wavelength is shown in Fig. 2.6. The vertical axis actually measures the

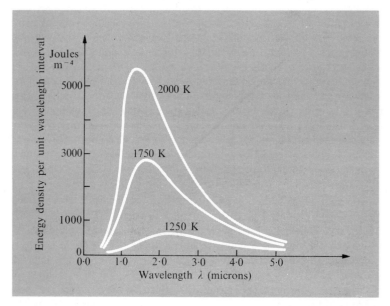

FIG. 2.6. The experimental radiation laws. The energy distribution curves for three different temperatures are shown. (The actual energy emitted per metre per second by the black body is obtained by multiplying the above values of energy density by the velocity of light.)

energy emitted per second per unit wavelength spread. It is seen that various curves are plotted in this figure, for different temperatures, and that although the general shape of the curve is the same in all cases, rising fairly steeply initially to a maximum, and then falling away somewhat more slowly on the longer-wavelength side, there is, nevertheless a definite shift in the position of the maximum as the temperature changes. These experimental results, as summarized in Fig. 2.6, represented the basic challenge associated with an understanding of the nature of radiation, since, for a very long time, all attempts to explain why these curves have the particular shape shown, met with complete failure. Thus, if the classical picture of radiation as a series of electromagnetic waves, as developed in the last section, were true, then this theory ought to be able to give a correct description of the distribution of energy in the waves emitted by a perfect emitter, or black body.

The classical approach—the Rayleigh–Jeans theory

An attempt to apply classical theory to just this problem was made by Rayleigh and Jeans, and their theory can be briefly summarized as follows. Without any loss in generalization, the black body can be considered as a real box, i.e. a cube with all sides of equal length, instead of as a sphere, since this configuration will be just as effective as absorbing the radiation entering from the small hole in the side, as would the spherical volume. The problem therefore resolves itself into calculating the energy which will be stored within such a box. When the box is raised above the temperature of its surroundings, the energy which will be emitted through the small hole in its side will be a sample of the energy contained within the box as a whole. The calculation of the possible waves within such a cube can probably be best approached by first considering the simpler one-dimensional case of waves on a stretched string. In this case standing waves, which can store energy, will be set up whenever an integral number of half-wavelengths can be fitted along the length of the string, L, as shown in Fig. 2.7(a),

$$\text{i.e.} \quad n\frac{\lambda}{2} = L \tag{2.7a}$$

For the wavelengths of greater than $L/10$ there will obviously be relatively few values per unit wavelength interval that can satisfy this condition, whereas for smaller and smaller wavelengths the number per unit wavelength interval will steadily increase, and approaches infinity as $\lambda \to 0$. If each allowed vibration has an equal amount of energy associated with it, there will then clearly be a high concentration of energy at the low wavelength, high-frequency end.

The same argument can now be applied to the standing waves in the three-dimensional box, and the only ones which will be able to store energy will be those which can be enclosed within the walls of the box, i.e. that can fit in an integral number of half-wavelengths between opposite walls. For radiation which is being reflected to and fro, parallel to one wall of the box, the condition for standing waves is exactly as for the string, i.e.

$$n\frac{\lambda}{2} = a \tag{2.7b}$$

where λ is the wavelength of the particular radiation, a is the length of the side of the box, and n is an integer. The longest-wavelength radiation that can be contained along this side of the box will then be equal to $2a$, and the next longest wavelength will be a and then there will be successively higher harmonics, with shorter wavelengths, as n increases in value. It is possible, however, for standing waves to exist along diagonals, and other directions, within the box as shown in Fig. 2.7(b) and the more general case must there-

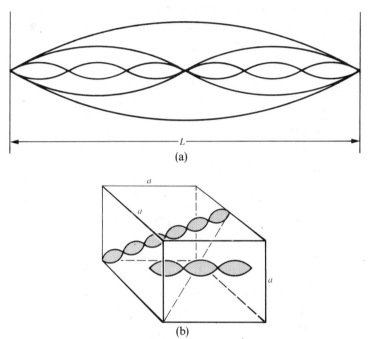

(a)

(b)

FIG. 2.7. Standing waves: (a) On a string of length L Standing waves for $n = 1, 2$, and 6 are shown. (b) For electromagnetic waves in a cube of side a. Only waves with an integral number of half-wavelengths fitting into the box can store energy.

fore be considered. This can be done as shown in Fig. 2.8 where one wavelength of the radiation is shown with its direction of propagation making directional cosines α, β, and γ with the three sides of the box.

One particular half-wavelength is shown and two planes are drawn normal to this at each end, and the points where they intersect the axes are shown. It can be seen by considering the projection of the half-wavelength on the x-axis that

$$x_1 = \frac{\lambda}{2} \cdot \frac{1}{\cos \alpha}, \qquad (2.8)$$

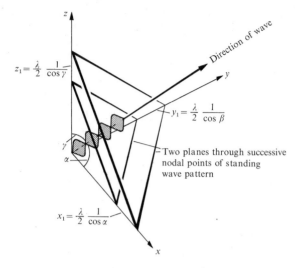

FIG. 2.8. Condition for standing wave in a general direction.

and it follows similarly that

$$y_1 = \frac{\lambda}{2} \cdot \frac{1}{\cos \beta} \qquad (2.9)$$

and

$$z_1 = \frac{\lambda}{2} \cdot \frac{1}{\cos \gamma}. \qquad (2.10)$$

The condition for such a wave to exist as a standing wave, and store energy, is that an integral number of x_1, y_1, and z_1 must fit along the side of the box, i.e. that

$$n_x x_1 = a \qquad n_y y_1 = a \qquad n_z z_1 = a \qquad (2.11)$$

where n_x, n_y, n_z are all integers. Hence the condition becomes

$$n_x = \frac{2a}{\lambda} \cos \alpha$$

$$n_y = \frac{2a}{\lambda} \cos \beta \qquad (2.12)$$

$$n_z = \frac{2a}{\lambda} \cos \gamma.$$

These three equations may now be squared and added to give

$$\left(\frac{2a}{\lambda}\right)^2 (\cos^2\alpha + \cos^2\beta + \cos^2\gamma) = n_x^2 + n_y^2 + n_z^2, \qquad (2.13)$$

and since the sum of the squares of the three direction cosines of any straight line add to unity, the condition becomes

$$\frac{2a}{\lambda} = [n_x^2 + n_y^2 + n_z^2]^{\frac{1}{2}}. \tag{2.14}$$

This equation therefore determines the particular wavelengths for which standing waves can exist and hence can store energy within the black body. In terms of allowed frequencies this becomes

$$v = \frac{c}{\lambda} = \frac{c}{2a} [n_x^2 + n_y^2 + n_z^2]^{\frac{1}{2}} \tag{2.15}$$

and the problem therefore resolves itself into a calculation of the number of sets of different integers, n_x, n_y, and n_z in the range $v \rightarrow (v + \delta v)$ that can meet the condition expressed in eqn (2.15).

The best way in which the number of such integers can be determined is to consider a three-dimensional net of integers as represented in Fig. 2.9. Here a

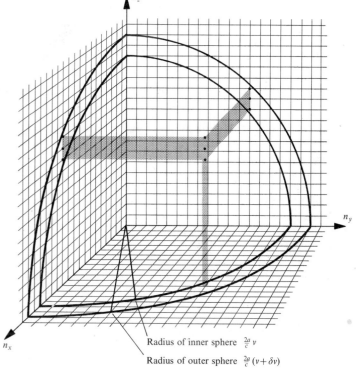

Radius of inner sphere $\frac{2a}{c} v$

Radius of outer sphere $\frac{2a}{c} (v + \delta v)$

FIG. 2.9. Net of integers to evaluate allowed frequencies.

projection is drawn from each integer along the x, y, and z-axis, and hence each black dot which denotes an intersection of such lines, represents a point which corresponds to integral values for n_x, n_y, and n_z. The number of such intersections in the range $v \rightarrow (v + \delta v)$ which can fulfil the conditions of eqn (2.15) may now be determined by drawing two spheres of radius $\dfrac{2a}{c} v$ and $\dfrac{2a}{c} (v + \delta v)$ on this diagram. The number of points, or intersections, which are then enclosed in the 'onion skin' between these two surfaces will be equal to the number of frequencies in the range between v and $(v + \delta v)$ which satisfy eqn (2.15). Waves with these allowed frequencies can therefore store energy in this frequency range within the black body.

This number can therefore be evaluated geometrically as being equal to the total volume in the onion skin covering one eighth of the sphere (since only positive integers are considered) divided by the volume of the unit cell formed by successive intersection points, which in this case is equal to unity, since the intersections occur at successive integral values. Hence the number of intersections within the volume, and thus the number of allowed frequencies, is given by $\frac{1}{8} . 4\pi r^2 . \delta r$ where r is the radius of the inner sphere. Therefore

$$\text{Number of allowed frequencies} = \frac{1}{8} . 4\pi \left(\frac{2a}{c} v \right)^2 \frac{2a}{c} . \delta v$$

$$= 4\pi a^3 . \frac{v^2}{c^3} . \delta v. \tag{2.16}$$

In fact this expression needs to be multiplied by two because electromagnetic waves are transverse waves and hence two can exist independently of each other along the same direction of propagation, if their vibrations are mutually at right angles.

The consideration of the geometrical properties of the space within the black body have therefore led to the conclusion that the number of frequencies in the range between v and $(v + \delta v)$, which can store electromagnetic energy, is given by

$$N_{v \rightarrow (v + \delta v)} = \frac{8\pi a^3 v^2}{c^3} \delta v. \tag{2.17}$$

The final step in the theory is to determine how much energy is to be associated with each of these frequencies, and a multiplication of these two factors will then give the total energy stored for the given frequency range, and hence the energy–wavelength distribution pattern.

This second step is, in fact, very straightforward in terms of classical physics since there is a very fundamental principle, or law, known as the 'Law of

Equipartition of Energy', which states that at an absolute temperature T, each type of motion or way of storing energy will have an energy of $\frac{1}{2}kT$ associated with it, where k is a universal constant, known as the Boltzmann constant, and is equal to the gas constant R divided by the Avogadro constant, N_A. The operation of this principle can probably be best illustrated by considering the specific heats of gases as an example.

In the kinetic theory of an ideal gas, the molecules may be considered as moving at random within a box, as illustrated in Fig. 2.10, and a particular

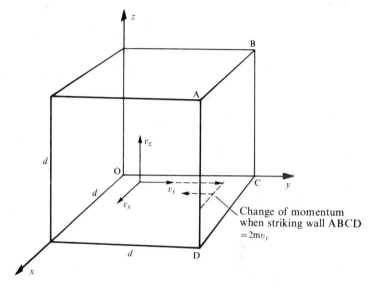

FIG. 2.10. Kinetic theory of an ideal gas. The arbitrary velocity v is resolved along the directions parallel to the three axes.

molecule may have velocity components v_x, v_y, and v_z along the three axes, as shown. The square of its total velocity would then be

$$v^2 = v_x^2 + v_y^2 + v_z^2. \tag{2.18}$$

In principle this equation could be written down for every molecule in the box, and the average of the squares of the velocities of all the molecules could then be obtained by summing both sides. We have

$$\overline{v^2} = \sum_{i=1}^{N} v_i^2/N = \overline{v_x^2} + \overline{v_y^2} + \overline{v_z^2} \tag{2.19}$$

where N is the total number of molecules in the box and the bar above the velocities indicates an average obtained by summing the values over all the N

different molecules, and then dividing by N. It is clear, from arguments of symmetry alone, that velocity components along the x-axis, must be just as likely as those along the y- or z-axis, and hence $\overline{v_x^2} = \overline{v_y^2} = \overline{v_z^2}$, and therefore $\overline{v^2} = 3\overline{v_x^2}$.

The relation between the velocities of the molecules and the pressure of the gas as a whole can be deduced by considering the change in momentum produced when an individual molecule, with velocity component v_x, hits the wall ABCD. The total change in its momentum parallel to the x-axis will then be $2mv_x$, and if the box is a cube of side d, the molecule will return, after reflection at the other end, to make another impact on the wall ABCD after a time $2d/v_x$. Hence the rate of its impact on this wall will be $v_x/2d$ per second, and the total change of its momentum in unit time, which by Newton's second law is equal to the force it exerts on the wall, is given by $(2mv_x) \times (v_x/2d)$.

It follows that the force on the wall due to the N molecules in the box will be

$$F = \sum_{i=1}^{N} \frac{m}{d} v_x^2 = \frac{Nm}{d} \overline{v_x^2}. \tag{2.20}$$

The pressure on the wall, P, will be the force divided by the area of ABCD, d^2, and substituting $\frac{1}{3}\overline{v^2}$ for $\overline{v_x^2}$ then gives

$$P = \frac{1}{3} \frac{Nm}{d^3} . \overline{v^2}. \tag{2.21}$$

If the mass of gas considered is a mole of the gas, M, so that N becomes the Avogadro constant, the volume d^3 can then be written as V, in the normal form of the gas equation to give

$$PV = \frac{1}{3}M\overline{v^2}. \tag{2.22}$$

Comparison of this equation with the ideal gas equation $PV = RT$ shows that these will be identical if $\frac{1}{3}M\overline{v^2} = RT$, i.e. if

$$\tfrac{1}{2}M\overline{v^2} = \tfrac{3}{2}RT. \tag{2.23}$$

The left-hand side measures the total kinetic energy of the gas molecules, and the equation therefore shows that this energy will increase linearly with temperature. Moreover the specific heat of the gas at constant volume is defined as the change of energy with temperature:

$$C_V = \frac{\partial}{\partial T}(\tfrac{3}{2}RT) = \tfrac{3}{2}R \quad (= 12.47 \text{ J mol}^{-1} \text{ K}^{-1}). \tag{2.24}$$

The measured specific heats of gases show that this value is indeed obtained for monatomic gases such as helium and argon, and that the total energy of a mole of such a gas is therefore given by the expression $\frac{3}{2}RT$, and that of individual molecule by the expression $\frac{3}{2}kT$.

We have already seen that each molecule has three independent velocity components, or 'degrees of freedom'. It has independent motion along the three coordinate axes, and thus the correct value for its total energy will be obtained if each degree of freedom has an energy of $\frac{1}{2}kT$ associated with it— which is in effect the statement of the law of equipartition of energy.

The only type of motion available to a gas formed of single monatomic molecules is translational motion which can be resolved along the three independent axes. Molecules of a diatomic gas can also rotate however, and these rotations can take place about two independent axes orientated at right angles to each other. Hence two additional types of motion, or 'ways of taking up energy', or degrees of freedom, become available, and each molecule should therefore have an energy of $5 \times (\frac{1}{2}kT)$, and the specific heat of the gas as a whole should be given by $\frac{5}{2}R \, (= 20 \cdot 79 \text{ J mol}^{-1} \text{ K}^{-1})$—which is indeed found to be the case for such gases as hydrogen and oxygen. Diatomic molecules can also vibrate but the vibrational energy levels are usually too far apart to introduce an additional contribution to the specific heat.

In more complex gaseous molecules further types of motion such as bending and stretching can also contribute to the specific heat, and in the crystalline lattice of a solid, atoms can vibrate about their mean position. Different degrees of freedom can be associated with all these different types of motion and it was found that the law of equipartition could be applied in a very general way to predict the total energy content, and hence also the specific heat, of all these different systems.

It can, moreover, also be applied to the particular case of electromagnetic waves, and, as with other types of simple harmonic motion involving the transfer of energy between two systems (electric and magnetic fields in this case), two degrees of freedom will be associated with this type of energy storage.

Eqn (2.17) gave the number of standing waves which could exist inside the 'black box' in the frequency range v to $(v + \delta v)$ and the law of equipartition of energy now states that each of these will store an energy of $2 \times (\frac{1}{2}kT)$, so that the total energy stored in the given frequency range may be written

$$E^{(T)}_{v \to (v + \delta v)} = \frac{8\pi a^3 v^2}{c^3} kT . dv \qquad (2.25)$$

or, since a^3 is the volume of the black body, in terms of energy per unit volume

$$E_{v \to (v + \delta v)} = \frac{8\pi v^2}{c^3} kT . dv. \qquad (2.26)$$

This is, in fact, one way in which the Rayleigh–Jeans law may be stated, or, if converted to a wavelength variation, noting that $\mathrm{d}v = -\dfrac{c}{\lambda^2}.\mathrm{d}\lambda$

$$E_{\lambda \to (\lambda - \delta\lambda)} = \frac{8\pi}{c^3}.kT.\frac{c^2}{\lambda^2}\frac{c}{\lambda^2}.\mathrm{d}\lambda$$

$$= 8\pi.kT.\lambda^{-4}\,\mathrm{d}\lambda. \tag{2.27}$$

The u.v. catastrophe and classical breakdown

This form of the Rayleigh–Jeans Law can be readily compared with the experimentally observed results, as is shown in Fig. 2.11, where good agree-

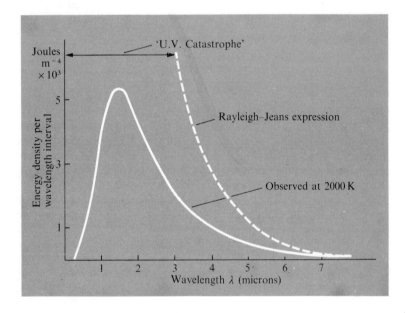

FIG. 2.11. Comparison of Rayleigh–Jeans law with experiment.

ment is found at large-wavelength values, but complete disagreement occurs for the very short wavelengths, i.e. at high frequencies. This complete disagreement came to be known as 'the ultraviolet catastrophe', since the Rayleigh–Jeans theory predicts an ever-increasing storage of energy in the shorter wavelengths of the spectrum. Moreover it is clear that this theory must be fundamentally incorrect since it not only completely disagrees with experiment at the shorter wavelengths, but also implies an infinite capacity of the radiation to store energy in this region.

Nevertheless it is clear that there are really only two basic assumptions in the Rayleigh–Jeans theory. The one assumption is that it is possible to calculate the number of wavelengths which will store energy within the box by applying the geometrical conditions of standing waves to them. The second assumption is that each of these standing waves will have an amount of energy equal to kT associated with it. Both of these assumptions seem to be absolutely valid, since the one depends only on the geometrical properties of three-dimensional space within the box, while the other had formed the basis of the whole of thermodynamics and of kinetic theory, as developed from a classical viewpoint. When approaching this problem, however, Planck realized that one or other of these basic assumptions must be wrong if there was such a complete contradiction between theory and experiment. He proceeded therefore to reconsider the whole model of radiation from first principles and see if there was any way in which the ultraviolet catastrophe could be avoided.

In considering the basic assumptions that had previously been made, it became clear that the one based on wavelength distribution as determined by the standing wave patterns, which were themselves determined by the geometrical properties of the box, would have to be accepted unless our basic understanding of the nature of space itself was to be overthrown. Planck therefore concentrated on the other fundamental assumption that the Rayleigh–Jeans model had made, which was concerned with the equal distribution of energy between the different wavelengths—i.e. the law of equipartition of energy. Instead of taking this as a fundamental postulate, Planck proceeded to consider the different energies that might be associated with each wavelength, and see how the total energy could be built up from these.

Equipartition of energy and the concept of quanta

If the general properties of a system are to be explained, there are normally two basic types of information that are required. One is the allowed energy levels that are available to the different components of the system. The other is the actual distribution of these components between the allowed energy levels. Thus, in the simple case of a monatomic gas, the allowed energy levels are just those associated with the kinetic energy of the moving molecules. The actual distribution of the molecules between these different energies is in fact given by the Maxwell–Boltzmann distribution curve. In diatomic gases rotational and vibrational energy levels also have to be considered, and the distribution of molecules amongst these then adds additional terms to such properties as the specific heat of the gas.

This is just one example of the way in which 'statistical mechanics' comes into physics, and the same general ideas can be applied to the energies of electromagnetic waves, as to those of gas molecules. In deriving the principle of equipartition of energy, which Rayleigh and Jeans had applied to deduce the mean energy associated with a wave of frequency, v, they had made two basic assumptions. The first was that the energy levels available to such a wave formed a continuum, so that the energy of the radiation could take any value from zero to an infinite amount. This was, of course, the essential concept of 'the classical wave' with energy steadily increasing, in proportion to its intensity. The second assumption was that the actual distribution of waves between the different available energy levels followed the same statistics as those of the perfect gas, and every other classical system that had been studied—i.e. the Boltzmann statistics.

The general ideas behind such a calculation can probably be best illustrated by taking the simple example of the distribution of three bricks on a step ladder. Imagine three bricks are thrown at such a step ladder standing vertically against the wall, with a total energy of four brick–step units, as illustrated in Fig. 2.12.

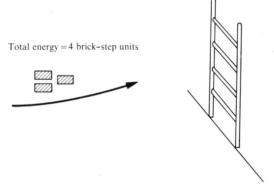

FIG. 2.12. Hypothetical experiment of throwing bricks at a ladder.

Thus it would then be possible for all the energy to go to one brick, and for this to end up on step 4, with the other two bricks, with zero energy, on the ground. It seems more 'likely', however, that the energy would be more equally shared amongst the bricks. The problem of statistical mechanics is to determine what is, in fact, the most likely distribution and hence the one that will occur in practice.

In order to do this two different concepts must be clearly differentiated— that of a DISTRIBUTION, and that of an ARRANGEMENT. A distribution defines the number of bricks (components) at different energy levels, without specifying which particular brick (component) is at which energy level; whereas an arrangement defines precisely which particular brick (component) is at which energy level. It is thus possible for several different arrangements to be included within the same distribution. This can be illustrated, for the simple case of the three bricks, in Fig. 2.13. The top of this figure illustrates

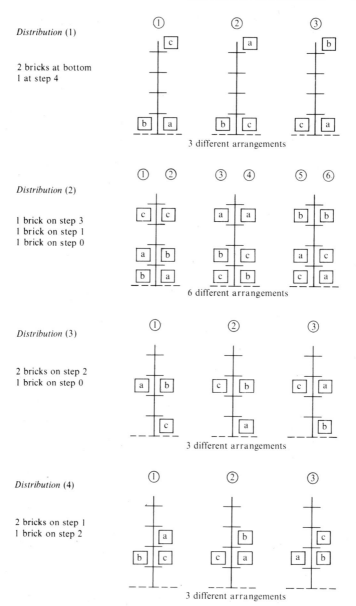

Distribution (1)

2 bricks at bottom
1 at step 4

3 different arrangements

Distribution (2)

1 brick on step 3
1 brick on step 1
1 brick on step 0

6 different arrangements

Distribution (3)

2 bricks on step 2
1 brick on step 0

3 different arrangements

Distribution (4)

2 bricks on step 1
1 brick on step 2

3 different arrangements

Fig. 2.13. Distribution and arrangements. An illustration of how these terms are employed in statistical mechanics—by reference to bricks on the ladder.

one particular distribution: Distribution (1)—two bricks at bottom, one at step 4. There are, however, three different arrangements of the individual bricks which will give rise to this one distribution. It will be seen that three other distributions (2), (3), and (4) can also be defined, and one of these has six different arrangements within it, while the other two have three.

In order to calculate which of these distributions is the most probable the basic assumption, or premise, of statistical mechanics is made: 'The most probable distribution is the one that has the largest number of arrangements associated with it'.

In the particular case of the bricks this will be distribution (2). One can in fact go further and say that the probability of finding this distribution is proportional to the number of arrangements producing it. Thus, in the case of the bricks, distribution (2) is twice as probable as any of the other distributions.

In the more general case the problem of finding the actual distribution of components between the various energy levels available resolves itself into finding the distribution which has the maximum number of arrangements giving rise to it.

Imagine different energy levels represented by boxes, as shown, where the first box has energy ε_1, with n_1 components (electrons or waves etc.) in it.

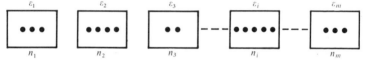

Let us concentrate first on a given *distribution*: $n_1, n_2, n_3, \ldots$ have fixed values for this given distribution. There are then two steps in the calculation:

(1) Calculate the number of *arrangements* which give rise to this distribution.

(2) Then consider other distributions as well and maximize this number by letting n_1, n_2, n_3 etc. vary. Thus find the most probable distribution, i.e. the one that exists in practice.

First we calculate the number of *arrangements*. In classical physics we assume electrons, atoms, waves, etc. can be distinguished from one another. In other words

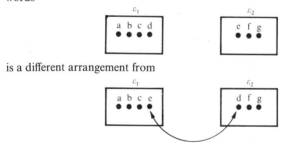

is a different arrangement from

but *not* from

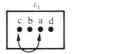

The total number of ways of arranging the entities in the energy levels will then be

$$\frac{N!}{n_1! \, n_2! \, n_3! \, \dots}$$

where $N!$ is the number of ways the total can be arranged among themselves and n_1 is the number of ways those in ε_1 can be rearranged amongst themselves. We can therefore say that the *probability* of finding this particular distribution is

$$P = \frac{N!}{n_1! \, n_2! \, \dots \, n_m!}. \tag{2.28}$$

Therefore the *actual* distribution will be the one that has a maximum value of P.

That is when $\ln\left[\dfrac{N!}{n_1! \, n_2! \, \dots \, n_m!}\right]$ has a maximum

or $\quad \ln N! - [\ln n_1! + \ln n_2! \, \dots \, \ln n_m!]$ has a maximum

or $\quad -[\ln n_1! + \ln n_2! \dots + \ln n_m!]$ has a minimum. $\quad$ (2.29)

To deal with this, we use Stirling's approximation.

$$\ln n! = n \ln n - n. \tag{2.30}$$

Therefore the condition for the most probable distribution becomes

$$-\delta[(n_1 \ln n_1 - n_1) + (n_2 \ln n_2 - n_2) \dots + (n_m \ln n_m - n_m)] = 0$$

or $\quad -\sum \delta(n_i \ln n_i) = 0 \quad$ which can be shown to be the same as

(i) $\qquad \displaystyle\sum_1^m \ln n_i \cdot \delta n_i = 0. \tag{2.31}$

There are two additional conditions.

Total number of particles is constant.

$$n_1 + n_2 + \dots n_m = N$$

(ii) $\qquad$ i.e. $\displaystyle\sum_1^m \delta n_i = 0. \tag{2.32}$

Total energy is constant.

$$n_1\varepsilon_1 + n_2\varepsilon_2 \ldots + n_m\varepsilon_m = E_{\text{TOTAL}}$$

(iii) $$\text{or } \sum_1^m \varepsilon_i\, \delta n_i = 0.$$ (2.33)

These three conditions are now combined in the *Method of Undetermined Multipliers.* This states that for an expression of the form,

$$\sum_1^m (\ln n_i + \alpha + \beta\varepsilon_i)\, \delta n_i = 0$$ (2.34)

where $n_i n_j n_k$ can be changed independently, it must follow that the equation is also true for all i separately.

$$\therefore \quad \ln n_i + \alpha + \beta\varepsilon_i = 0$$
$$\therefore \quad \ln n_i = -\alpha - \beta\varepsilon_i$$
$$n_i = e^{-\alpha}e^{-\beta\varepsilon_i}$$ (2.35)
$$n_i = Ce^{-\beta\varepsilon_i}$$

which is represented schematically in Fig. 2.14. It can be shown by applying

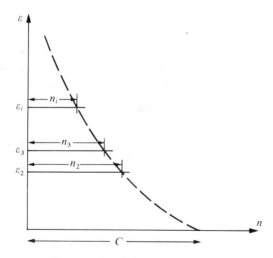

FIG. 2.14. The Boltzmann distribution.

this equation to the energy distribution in an ideal gas that

$$\beta = \frac{1}{kT}.$$ (2.36)

Substitution of this then gives the usual form of the Boltzmann Distribution

$$n_i = Ce^{-\varepsilon_i/kT}. \tag{2.37}$$

Although it is now known that this statistical distribution is in fact an approximation, and more sophisticated quantum statistics have to be applied in some cases, the Boltzmann expression is a very good approximation in a large number of cases. At the time Planck had no reason to assume that it would not be appropriate to apply this to the energy distribution of the waves. This being so, there was only one other fundamental assumption left to query, i.e. that the energy levels available to the waves formed a continuum. In challenging this assumption Planck produced the concept of quantization of energy—the possibility that a system could not change its energy in continuous amounts, but only in a series of discrete values, or jumps. The other fundamentally new idea linked by Planck with this concept was that the magnitude of such energy jumps should be proportional to the frequency of the radiation emitted—equal to $h\nu$ where h was to be a universal constant, and to be known as the Planck constant.

The net effect that this new concept has on the calculation of the energy distribution with wavelength can probably be best considered by running the classical and quantum treatments side by side and comparing the different steps. Thus both theories accept the purely geometrical calculation of the allowed standing wave patterns within the box of the black body, and hence both accept eqn (2.17) as determining the *number* of allowed frequencies within the specified frequency range.

The difference between the two theories will come from the average energy to be associated with these allowed frequencies. The two situations can probably be best represented as in Fig. 2.15, where the classical picture of the

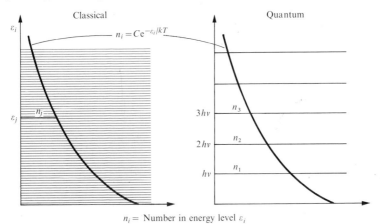

$n_i = $ Number in energy level ε_i

FIG. 2.15. The classical and quantum pictures of allowed energy levels with a Boltzmann distribution.

energies available to the electromagnetic wave is shown on the left hand side as a continuum of levels, while the quantum picture is shown on the right hand side as a series of discrete levels spaced hv apart.

In both cases the average energy of the system can be calculated by (i) applying Boltzmann statistics to determine the number of components in each energy level, and (ii) summing the product of this number with the corresponding energy for each level, and then dividing this by the total number of components. The average energy of the system will therefore be given by

$$\bar{\varepsilon} = \sum_{i=0}^{\infty} n_i \varepsilon_i \Big/ \sum_{i=0}^{\infty} n_i \qquad (2.38)$$

where n_i is the number of waves with energy ε_i and is given by eqn (2.35).

The classical assumption implies a continuum of energy levels and the summation becomes an integration, whereas a discrete summation remains for the quantum model. The two calculations therefore proceed as below.

CLASSICAL	QUANTUM

CLASSICAL

$$\bar{\varepsilon} = \dfrac{\displaystyle\int_0^{\infty} \varepsilon_i C e^{-\varepsilon_i/kT}\, \mathrm{d}\varepsilon}{\displaystyle\int_0^{\infty} C e^{-\varepsilon_i/kT}\, \mathrm{d}\varepsilon}.$$

Integrating by parts gives

$$\bar{\varepsilon} = \dfrac{\left[-\varepsilon kT e^{-\varepsilon/kT} + \displaystyle\int kT e^{-\varepsilon/kT}\, \mathrm{d}\varepsilon\right]_0^{\infty}}{[-kT e^{-\varepsilon/kT}]_0^{\infty}}$$

$$= \dfrac{[-kT e^{-\varepsilon/kT}[\varepsilon + kT]]_0^{\infty}}{kT}$$

$$= \dfrac{(kT)^2}{kT}$$

$$\therefore \quad \bar{\varepsilon} = kT.$$

QUANTUM

$$\bar{\varepsilon} = \dfrac{\displaystyle\sum_0^{\infty} \varepsilon_i C e^{-\varepsilon_i/kT}}{\displaystyle\sum_0^{\infty} C e^{-\varepsilon_i/kT}}.$$

The quantum condition is that ε_i can only equal $hv, 2hv, \ldots$

Let $\qquad x = e^{-hv/kT}$.

Then $\qquad x^2 = e^{-2hv/kT}$ etc.

$$\therefore \quad \bar{\varepsilon} = \dfrac{hvx + 2hvx^2 + 3hvx^3 + \ldots}{1 + x + x^2 + x^3 + \ldots}$$

$$= \dfrac{hvx(1 + 2x + 3x^2 + \ldots)}{1 + x + x^2 + x^3 + \ldots}.$$

By the Binomial theorem the numerator is $\dfrac{hvx}{(1-x)^2}$, and the denominator is a simple G.P. equal to $\dfrac{1}{(1-x)}$.

$$\therefore \quad \bar{\varepsilon} = \dfrac{hvx}{(1-x)^2} \cdot (1-x) = \dfrac{hv}{\dfrac{1}{x} - 1}.$$

$$\therefore \quad \bar{\varepsilon} = hv/(e^{hv/kT} - 1).$$

Hence the classical theory gives

$$\bar{\varepsilon} = kT \tag{2.39}$$

while the quantum theory gives

$$\bar{\varepsilon} = \frac{hv}{(e^{hv/kT} - 1)}. \tag{2.40}$$

It is seen that the kT of the law of equipartition of energy does indeed follow from the classical approach, but that if the concept of quantization of energy is introduced then the expression for the mean energy changes significantly. If however $hv \ll kT$, as would be the case for the larger wavelengths, then the mean energy can be written as

$$\bar{\varepsilon} \approx \frac{hv}{\left[1 + \dfrac{hv}{kT} \cdots \right] - 1} \approx kT \tag{2.41}$$

and hence agreement with the classical approach and the Rayleigh–Jeans theory is obtained in the long-wavelength region.

Planck's theory and equations

It is clear that as the frequency increases the approximation $hv \ll kT$ no longer holds, and then the full expression for the average energy of eqn (2.40) must be taken. The accurate expression for the energy–wavelength distribution will then be obtained by taking eqn (2.17) and (2.40) together to give the energy density in the frequency range v to $(v + \delta v)$.

$$E_{v \to (v + \delta v)} = \frac{8\pi v^2}{c^3} \cdot \frac{hv}{e^{hv/kT} - 1} \cdot dv$$

$$E_{v \to (v + \delta v)} = \frac{8\pi h}{c^3} \cdot \frac{v^3}{(e^{hv/kT} - 1)} \cdot dv, \tag{2.42}$$

or in terms of wavelength variation

$$E_{\lambda \to (\lambda - \delta \lambda)} = 8\pi \cdot \lambda^{-4} \cdot \frac{h \dfrac{c}{\lambda}}{e^{hc/\lambda kT} - 1} \cdot d\lambda$$

$$E_{\lambda \to (\lambda - \delta \lambda)} = \frac{8\pi hc}{\lambda^5} \cdot \frac{1}{(e^{hc/\lambda kT} - 1)} \cdot d\lambda. \tag{2.43}$$

This last equation is in fact the now famous expression derived by Planck to explain the observed variation of energy with wavelength and a comparison of the curve predicted by this expression, and that observed experimentally, shows extremely good agreement. Planck was thus not only able to avoid the ultraviolet catastrophe by his introduction of the concept of quantized energy, but also to produce a theory which gave precise quantitative agreement with experimental observations.

The value of the constant h can, of course, be adjusted to give the best fit between the predicted and observed curves for one selected temperature, but when once determined in this way, it is found that the same value then also gives the best fit for all the curves at other temperatures. Moreover, later work, such as that on the photoelectric effect discussed below, showed that this constant was indeed a universal constant—and always defined the energy content of a quantum of electromagnetic radiation as $h\nu$.

Thus in successfully explaining the nature of this radiation law, Planck had to introduce the concept of a quantization of energy, and assume that in the process of absorption and emission, energy could not be exchanged in continuous, or unspecified amounts, but must always be exchanged in units or quanta which were given by a definite constant times the frequency of the radiation. This introduction of quantization into energy was as great an advance in the conceptual framework of physics as the concept of atomicity in the structure of matter, but because of the rather mathematical way in which the concept was first introduced, relatively little notice was taken of it for the first few years of its existence. Other scientists, although recognizing that Planck had managed to produce a theory that agreed with the experimental results, felt on the whole that this was more of a mathematical device than a major reappraisal of the nature of radiation. It awaited the genius of Einstein a few years later, to take up this new concept and show that it could be used to explain other important phenomena, before the insight of Planck himself came to be fully recognized and appreciated.

PROBLEMS

2.1. How many different wavelengths in the range between 4 000 and 4 010 Å (i.e. 400–410 nm) can exist as standing waves in a cube of length 10^{-1} m?

2.2. It has been seen that the specific heat of a monatomic gas is $3R/2$ and that of a diatomic is $5R/2$. What specific heat is predicted by the Law of Equipartition of Energy for a solid in which each atom has two degrees of freedom associated with vibrational motion along any given direction?

2.3. If four bricks had been thrown at the ladder in the example given on p. 34, and their total energy was six brick–step units, calculate (i) the different number of 'distributions' that can exist, (ii) which 'distribution' is the most likely to occur, and (iii) how much more probable this one is than the next most probable distribution.

2.4. One of the excited states of the hydrogen atom lies $82\,277$ cm^{-1} above the ground state. What fraction of hydrogen atoms will be in this excited state at temperatures of (i) 100 K (ii) 300 K (iii) 1 000 K (iv) 10 000 K?

2.5. Derive an expression from the Planck radiation formula for the wavelength which corresponds to the maximum in energy density. What will this wavelength be for temperatures of (i) 1 000 K (ii) 3 000 K (iii) 10 000 K?

2.6. By integrating the Planck radiation formula over all frequencies, or wavelengths, show that the variation of total power emitted by a black body varies as T^4.

2.7. Above what wavelengths does the Rayleigh–Jeans expression approach within 20 per cent of Planck's expression for the energy density at temperatures of (i) 1 000 K (ii) 3 000 K (iii) 10 000 K?

2.8. Calculate the average (root-mean-square) velocity of (i) hydrogen molecules, (ii) oxygen molecules at (a) room temperature (27°C) and (b) 327°C given that the atomic weight of hydrogen is approximately 1 and oxygen is 16. How many impacts per second would such molecules, striking a wall normally, have to make to exert a pressure of 1 atmosphere (10^5 Newton.m^{-2})?

2.9. In Problem 2.2 the specific heat of a solid insulator, comprised of vibrating atoms fixed in a crystal structure was calculated. What additional heat would Classical Physics predict for a metal in which electrical conduction is assumed to take place via a gas of free electrons existing inside the metal?

2.10. Calculate the ratio of the population of the excited states given below, to their ground state if they are in thermal equilibrium at room temperature (27°C):
   (i) the gas rotational energy state with $J = 4$ of Problem 1.8.
   (ii) the electronic state of the higher neon level in the gas laser of Problem 1.9.
   (iii) the excited nuclear level of the iron nucleus in Problem 1.11.
   (iv) the upper of the two levels in the electron resonance transition of Problem 1.12.

2.11. Derive Stirling's approximation that

$$\ln n! = n \ln n - n$$

for large values of n.

2.12. Show that the statement on page 37 that

$$\sum \delta(n_i \ln n_i) = \sum \ln n_i \cdot \delta n_i$$

is in fact true.

3. The photoelectric effect and the localized wave packet

Photoelectric effect—discovery

ONE of the very interesting and slightly ironic points about the history of atomic physics is that the crucial experiments conducted by Hertz in order to confirm the ideas of Maxwell also, quite by accident, set in motion another series of investigations which eventually led to the overthrow of the classical theory of radiation and produced the most convincing evidence for its quantum properties. Thus in order to demonstrate the existence of the electromagnetic waves predicted theoretically by Maxwell, Hertz set up a transmitter in which a spark was produced between two metal spheres. The spheres were connected to a circuit, containing inductance and capacitance, which was capable of producing electrical oscillations. He was able to show that whenever a spark jumped across the gap between the spheres, electromagnetic waves were produced which could then be picked up some distance away. This was demonstrated by a loop of wire containing a small gap across which small sparks were produced when the electromagnetic waves were received. In this way, Hertz was able to show that the electromagnetic waves so produced had all the same basic properties as light waves, and hence he was able to verify quite precisely Maxwell's predictions on electromagnetic radiation.

However, he also noticed, in passing, that the spark that was induced across the gap in the receiving coil could be obtained more easily if this gap was illuminated with ultraviolet light. Although Hertz himself did not follow up this particular observation in more detail, one of his students, Hallwachs proceeded to show that this was part of a general effect: i.e. a negatively charged metal plate could be made to lose its charge when illuminated with ultraviolet light. These experiments were, in essence, the discovery of the photoelectric effect, although at that time the concept of electrons being emitted from the surface was not, of course, appreciated. However, a little later, in 1899, Lenard showed that it was indeed electrons that were emitted when the metal surface was illuminated. This was demonstrated by adapting the classic experiment of J. J. Thomson, who established the nature of the electrons by studying the deflection of the beam produced from a gas discharge tube when magnetic and electric fields were applied to it. Thus Lenard was able to show that the curvature produced in the path of the particles emitted from the illuminated metal surface after they had been accelerated by a known potential difference had exactly the same value in an applied magnetic field as that expected for electrons.

Current, voltage, and frequency characteristics

Lenard then went on to study in detail the characteristics of the photo-electric current which could be obtained from such an illuminated surface, and the basic apparatus used in this work is illustrated in Fig. 3.1. The metal

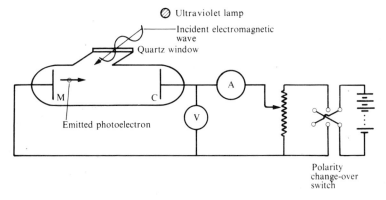

FIG. 3.1. Basic apparatus for studying the photoelectric effect.

surface is illuminated with ultraviolet light which passes through the quartz window as shown, and the photoelectrons which are then emitted from the surface, M, are collected by the plate, C, these two being enclosed in a vacuum. Various voltages can be applied to the collecting plate as indicated by the circuit, but the plate is normally held at a positive potential so that the photoelectrons are attracted across to it. The current so produced can be measured by the ammeter.

If both the frequency and intensity of the u.v. illumination are held constant, and the magnitude of the current is plotted against the value of the potential difference between the plates, then a typical set of results will be obtained as shown in Fig. 3.2. It will be seen that when the collector plate is sufficiently positive, the photoelectric current settles down to a steady saturation value, this indicating that all the photoelectrons which are being emitted from the illuminated surface are reaching the collector plate, and no further increase in current can therefore be expected. However, as the potential falls, the photoelectric current itself begins to drop. If the electrons were emitted from the surface with zero velocity, and only acquired kinetic energy due to the electric field between the plates, it would follow that the photoelectric current should fall to precisely zero, when there was no electric field between the two plates. However, it is clear from reference to Fig. 3.2 that this is not the case. Even when the potential difference between the plates is zero there is still a significant photoelectric current passing between them. In fact a definite

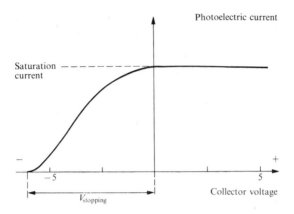

FIG. 3.2. Current–voltage characteristics of collector circuit.

negative potential difference has to be applied between the plates in order to reduce the photoelectric current to zero. This potential is normally called $V_{stopping}$, and abbreviated to V_s, and must measure the energy with which the electrons are ejected from the metal surface. Thus electrons emerging with a finite velocity will be able to move against the negative potential on the collector plate unless this is of such a value to nullify their motion completely, when $\frac{1}{2}mv_{max}^2$ will be equal to eV_s. The measurement of V_s is thus a very direct way of determining the maximum kinetic energy which the photoelectrons have as they leave the metal surface.

The above characteristics have been plotted for constant intensity and frequency of the incident illumination, but other interesting results are obtained if the variation of the photoelectric current with these parameters is also studied. One characteristic that is of particular importance is the way in which the value of V_s, and thus the maximum kinetic energy of the ejected electrons, varies with the intensity and frequency of the incident illumination. Before discussing the results in detail, the theory of the photoelectric effect, as given by Maxwell's classical wave picture, must first be considered.

Classical predictions and contradictions

The emission of the photoelectrons can be very readily explained in terms of the classical picture of electromagnetic waves, as is schematically represented in Fig. 3.3. Here the electric vector of the incident electromagnetic wave is shown interacting with a free electron in the metal conductor, and the oscillations of this electric vector will produce corresponding oscillations in the electron motion. As the wave continues to fall on the metal surface, so more

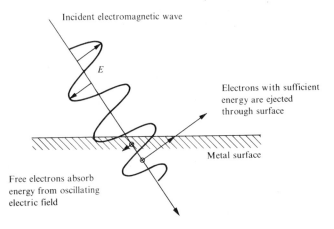

Incident electromagnetic wave

E

Electrons with sufficient
energy are ejected
through surface

Metal surface

Free electrons absorb
energy from oscillating
electric field

FIG. 3.3. Classical model of the photoelectric effect.

energy will be transferred to the electron, and once these oscillations are large enough to overcome the forces holding the electron within the solid, it will be ejected through the surface, thus forming the photoelectron. The energy required to break through the surface of the metal is normally measured in terms of a work function, and can be readily defined in units of electronvolts. It is then found that a typical metal surface will have a work function of a few electron volts magnitude.

At first sight, this simple picture of the mechanism of the photoelectric effect seems to explain the observed phenomenon. Each electron will need to absorb a certain amount of energy from the electromagnetic wave before it can overcome the work function at the surface, but having absorbed this amount it is then ejected to form part of the photoelectric current. However, closer study of this theory shows that its predictions are in no way verified by experiment. Thus the energy acquired by the electron via this mechanism will depend on the one hand on the intensity of the incoming electromagnetic wave, and on the other on the time during which the absorption takes place. It would therefore appear that the crucial parameter determining whether photoelectrons are to be produced in a given circumstance, or not, will be the intensity of the u.v. illumination. Moreover one can perform a simple order of magnitude calculation to determine the time that should elapse before sufficient energy has been absorbed for a single electron to be emitted. If the case of a lamp emitting one watt of radiation in the ultraviolet region placed a metre away from the metal surface is taken as typical then the energy density falling on the surface will be about 10^{-1} joule m^{-2} s^{-1}. If the area of absorption for one electron is taken as that corresponding to the outer radius of the atom, then the rate of energy absorption by the electron will be approximately 10^{-21} joules s^{-1} and hence for it to overcome a work function of 1 eV, it will need to absorb radiation for a period of approximately $10^{-19} \times 10^{21}$ s, i.e. about 2 minutes.

When these predictions of the classical theory are compared with the actual experimental results, not only is there a lack of agreement between them, but there is in fact a complete contradiction. Thus it is found on the one hand that the energy of the emitted photoelectrons does not depend on the intensity of the incoming radiation at all, but instead it depends crucially on its frequency, which is not a relevant parameter in the classical picture. And on the other hand it is found that instead of having to wait for a period of about one minute after the radiation is turned on, before any photoelectrons are emitted, instead they appear to be ejected absolutely instantaneously with no time lag at all. It would therefore appear that the classical picture, or model, of the photoelectric effect must be very badly astray, and it was against this background that Einstein produced his theory of the effect, with the concept of the localized wave packet.

Einstein's concept of the localized wave packet

It was Einstein's explanation of the photoelectric effect that really convinced scientists in general of the truth of the quantum concept. This had already been introduced theoretically by Planck in explaining the radiation laws, but appeared in that context to be more of a mathematical device than a physical concept. Einstein appreciated that the crucial fact to explain in the photoelectric effect was the dependence of the energy of emitted photoelectrons on the frequency of the incoming illumination, rather than on its intensity. These particular results are summarized in Fig. 3.4, where the maximum energy of the emitted photoelectron, as determined by the measurement of the stopping voltage V_s, is plotted against the frequency of the incident illumination. Two striking features emerge from this experimental measurement. The first is that there is a definite cut-off frequency and once the frequency of illumination falls below a certain value, no photoelectrons are emitted, however intense the radiation. The second crucial point is that the variation of stopping voltage with frequency is accurately linear i.e. there is a linear relationship between the maximum energy of the emitted photoelectron and the frequency of the illumination. Einstein appreciated that this was another way of representing Planck's postulate that the atomic oscillators emitted and absorbed radiation in energy quanta, the magnitude of which was proportional to the frequency. Moreover if this concept of quantized emission and absorption is now carried over and applied to the wave as travelling through space, then an explanation of the photoelectric effect might become possible. Thus Einstein's great contribution, in this context, was to associate the concept of quantized energy with a localized wave packet moving through space, as well as with the

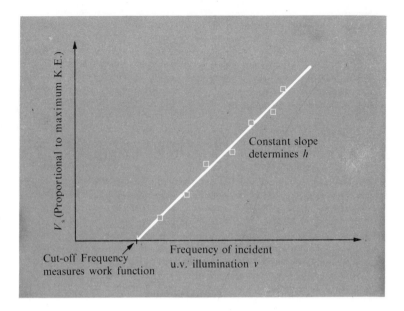

FIG. 3.4. Variation of stopping voltage (and hence maximum kinetic energy of photoelectrons) with frequency.

absorption and emission processes themselves. The model of the u.v. illumination falling on the metal surface thus became that of a series of wave packets, each containing an energy $h\nu$, rather than the picture of a continuous oscillating electromagnetic vector of Maxwell. These two models are contrasted diagrammatically in Fig. 3.5, and it is evident that they will imply quite different predictions for the characteristics of the emitted photoelectric current.

Thus, on the new quantum picture proposed by Einstein, the emission of a photoelectron will depend entirely on the energy contained within each incident wave packet, since if one of these has not sufficient energy, neither will any other wave packet of the same frequency. The possibility of emission of the photoelectron thus depends entirely on the frequency of the radiation and not on the number of wave packets arriving at the surface (i.e. the intensity of the incoming radiation). Moreover the instantaneous emission of the photoelectrons is now also explained, since all the energy of the individual wave packet will be instantaneously transferred to the absorbing electron, and the first photoelectron will be emitted as soon as the first wave packets strike the metal surface and thus no build-up time is required.

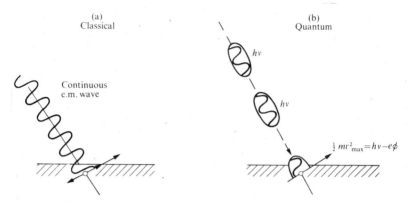

FIG. 3.5. Comparison of classical and quantum models of the photoelectric effect. (a) Electrons continuously absorb energy from oscillating electric field of incident e.m. wave. (b) Energy arrives in wave packets of magnitude $h\nu$. Absorption of one of these gives individual electron $h\nu$ inside metal and $(h\nu - e\phi)$ after leaving surface.

The photoelectric equation

The basic features of Einstein's theory of the photoelectric effect can be summarized readily in a straightforward mathematical equation, i.e.

$$eV_s = \tfrac{1}{2}mv_{max}^2 = h\nu - e\phi. \tag{3.1}$$

The first two parts of this equation represent the two different expressions for the maximum kinetic energy of the emitted photoelectron, measured either in terms of the electric potential difference required to bring it to rest, or in terms of its mass and velocity. The Einstein theory then predicts that this kinetic energy will be equal to the energy of the incident quantum, i.e. $h\nu$, less the minimum energy required to escape from the metal surface, which is measured by the work function as explained before and denoted by the symbol ϕ. The value of the work function is usually quoted in units of electron-volts, and such units can be used throughout the equation above. Alternatively, the calculations are often carried through in terms of joules, as energy units, and the use of both of these systems of units is illustrated in the examples that follow.

The precise accuracy of this photoelectric equation was verified in detail by the work of Millikan in 1916, but the general idea which was propounded by Einstein in 1905 was rapidly accepted, since it so obviously accounted for the main features of the effect, which completely contradicted the classical model.

PROBLEMS

3.1. If light of wavelength 250 nm is incident on a metal surface electrons are emitted which can just be prevented from reaching a collecting electrode if a retarding potential of 0·77 volts is applied. Calculate the photoelectric work function of the metal.

3.2. H_α radiation (of 656 nm wavelength), from a lamp containing atomic hydrogen, falls on a metal surface which has a work function of 2·0 electronvolts. The photoelectrons emitted from this surface are collected on a charged electrode. Calculate the minimum retarding potential that will prevent any of the electrons reaching the anode.

3.3. Calculate the critical wavelength of incident radiation for the emission of photoelectrons from a metal with work function of 3·5 electronvolts. What wavelength of incident radiation is necessary for the ejected photoelectrons to have a maximum velocity of (i) $0·1c$ (ii) $0·9c$?

3.4. On the classical theory of the photoelectric effect the electromagnetic waves falling on an area approximately equal to that of an atom (i.e. a circle of 10^{-10} m diameter) are absorbed and their energy is then available to eject a photoelectron. If the binding energy which such an electron has to overcome before ejection is 3 electron volts, calculate the time taken for sufficient energy to be absorbed from a lamp placed 1 m away and emitting 1 watt of radiation isotropically in the u.v. region.

3.5. On the quantum theory the u.v. radiation from the lamp in Problem 3.4. would consist of a stream of photons. If the radiation were all emitted at a wavelength of 1 216 Å, calculate the number of photons that would be leaving the lamp each second.

3.6. Calculate the number of photons emitted per second from the following sources, assuming that each is radiating power at 100 watt at the wavelength in question:
   (i) a yellow sodium street lamp, given that the yellow line of atomic sodium has a wavelength of 5 890 Å.
   (ii) a helium–neon laser operating at a wavelength of 6 300 Å.
   (iii) an X-ray tube emitting line spectra at 0·75 Å.
   (iv) the γ-ray source of Problem 1.11.

3.7. It will be seen in Chapter 5 that, as well as having a discrete amount of energy, $h\nu$, associated with it, each photon also has a discrete amount of linear momentum $h\nu/c$. Assuming this to be the case, show, by considering the conservation of energy and linear momentum, that a 'third body' must be present for the photoelectric effect to take place—i.e. that a photon of electromagnetic radiation cannot transfer all of its energy to a single free electron.

4. The quantized atom—the Bohr theory

The Rutherford model

AT the same time as a deeper understanding of the nature of energy and radiation was being developed, so a more precise picture and model of the nature of the atom was also coming into existence. The work of J. J. Thomson at the turn of the century on the deflection of cathode rays in gas discharge tubes had established the identity and universal nature of the electron as one of the fundamental constituents of all matter, and his later work on the deflection of positive ions had shown that the great majority of the mass of each atom was always associated with the positive ion left behind when the electrons had been stripped from it. This led J. J. Thomson to put forward the first model of the atom in the form of a 'plum pudding' or 'jelly' of positive material in which the electrons were embedded somewhat like currants. This model of the atom is shown diagrammatically in Fig. 4.1(a), and although from today's viewpoint it may appear very naive, it should be remembered that at that time it could explain all the known properties of the individual atom. Thus ionization in a gas discharge tube could be envisaged as just the displacement of individual electrons from their position within the jelly-like structure to leave the rest of the atom as the positive ion.

It was Rutherford who suggested in 1911 after early experiments on the scattering of α-particles (helium nuclei) that the correct model of the atom was of an entirely different nature: instead of the heavy positive material being uniformly distributed in the form of a jelly, it was in fact concentrated into a very small volume in the form of a nucleus, and rather than being embedded in this the electrons circled the nucleus in orbits rather like planets around the sun. Although both of these models could explain the results of the gas discharge studies, there were other sets of experiments which could distinguish between them—in particular the studies on the scattering of α-particles by thin films of gold. These experiments and their implications are considered in detail by G. K. T. Conn in *Atoms and their structure* (OPS 6), but the different kinds of deflection that might be expected for the two models are shown diagrammatically in Fig. 4.1, where the two are contrasted.

Thus an α-particle approaching a layer of atoms of the Thomson type will need to pass through an individual atom, since these extend to fill all the available space. In passing through the positive jelly, however, it will not suffer any sudden, or large, deflection since the positive charge is uniformly distributed in the volume and hence a relatively minor effect on the path of the alpha particle is to be expected. The deflection produced by the electrons

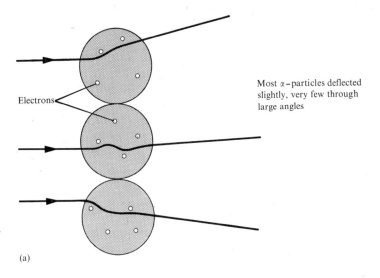

Most α–particles deflected
slightly, very few through
large angles

Electrons

(a)

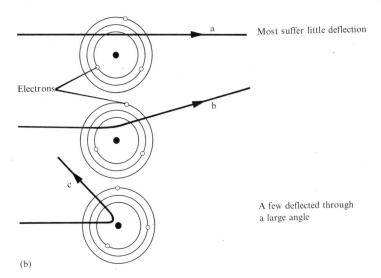

Most suffer little deflection

Electrons

A few deflected through
a large angle

(b)

FIG. 4.1. α-Particle scattering by different models of the nucleus. (a) 'Plum pudding'
of J. J. Thomson. (b) Nuclear model of Rutherford.

embedded within the atom will also only be very small because, although localized, they themselves are much lighter than the α-particle. As a result of its passage through such a diffuse atom the α-particle's track is likely to be deflected through only a very small angle, and any major deflection will be extremely rare.

In contrast, an α-particle which approaches a layer of atoms of the Rutherford type will in most cases meet empty space, and only suffer very small deflections from the light orbiting electrons. However, if the path of the α-particle approaches close to the position of the nucleus itself, then quite major forces come into play since the whole of the positive charge of the nucleus is concentrated effectively at a single point. There will therefore be an inverse square law repulsion between the α-particle and the nucleus. Although at reasonable distances only somewhat small deflections are produced, as indicated by the path b in Fig. 4.1, it is nevertheless possible for a particle which approaches close to the nucleus to experience a very large repulsive force and be deflected by more than 90° as indicated by the path c. There is, therefore, a very crucial and straightforward test between the validity of these two models which can be carried out by firing a beam of α-particles at a layer of atoms as in a thin gold foil. If nearly all the α-particles are scattered through only a small angle, then it would appear that Thomson's model is correct. Whereas if a significant number are found to be deflected through large angles and even back towards the direction from which they originated, then this must imply a small centre of very strong repulsion such as envisaged in Rutherford's nuclear atom. Such experiments were then carried out by two of Rutherford's research students, Geiger and Marsden, in 1911, shortly after Rutherford proposed the model, and these measurements proved conclusively that the nuclear model was in fact correct. The experiments not only confirmed that some α-particles were indeed scattered back through more than 90°, but also that the detailed angular variation of the scattering followed that predicted by Rutherford's theory. (For further details of these measurements and calculations see *Atoms and their structure* by Conn.)

Therefore, by 1912, the basic models of both the nature of energy and radiation on the one hand, and of the structure of the atom, on the other, were established. However, within a few months of the crucial experiments demonstrating the validity of Rutherford's model, it ran into very serious difficulties when it was used in an attempt to explain the nature and origin of the spectral lines that are observed from atoms.

Spectral lines and their explanation

The study of spectral lines emitted from atoms and their eventual explanation is a very good example of the scientific method in action and also forms one of the corner stones in the development of the ideas of atomic physics. From the 1850s the discrete absorption and emission lines that can be observed in the spectra from atoms excited in a gaseous state had been observed, and a large amount of empirical data was accumulated in these early years. The first advance towards an understanding of their nature came when J. J. Balmer was able to show that the spectral lines from atomic hydrogen could be fitted to a simple and precise equation given by

$$\bar{v} = R\left(\frac{1}{n_1^2} - \frac{1}{n_2^2}\right). \tag{4.1}$$

In this expression $\bar{v}$ represents the wavenumber, defined as the inverse of the wavelength or the number of waves in one metre, while n_1 and n_2 are integers. In the particular series studied by Balmer which were the lines from atomic hydrogen falling in the visible region of the spectrum, he concentrated on the series which had a value $n_1 = 2$ for the first term, and was then able to show that he could fit in all the other members of this series by letting n_2 run with integral values from 3 upwards. The constant R† remained the same for each spectral line on the series, and experimental fitting of this value to the lines gave the empirical magnitude of $1 \cdot 0968 \times 10^7 \text{ m}^{-1}$.

The actual series of spectral lines observed and correlated by Balmer in this way is shown in Fig. 4.2, and the successively smaller difference in energy

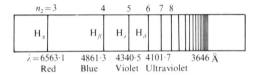

FIG. 4.2. Balmer series of lines observed from atomic hydrogen.

between them is clearly evident, this arising from the successively smaller differences between the inverse of integers squared. It will also be clear from both the diagram and the expression of eqn (4.1) that a series limit is rapidly approached as n_2 becomes large, and the lines will converge onto a wavenumber given by $R(1/2^2)$, i.e. onto $R/4$ in the case of the Balmer series.

Following this empirical discovery by Balmer, other workers were then able to show that a similar type of expression could be used to correlate other series of lines observed from atomic hydrogen. Thus Lyman found a series in the ultraviolet which could be represented by the expression

$$\bar{v} = R\left(\frac{1}{1^2} - \frac{1}{n_2^2}\right) \tag{4.2}$$

where n_2 has values 2, 3, 4 etc., and later, in 1908, Paschen found another

† Often written as R_∞.

series of exactly similar form in the infrared, which could be fitted to the expression

$$\bar{v} = R\left(\frac{1}{3^2} - \frac{1}{n_2^2}\right). \tag{4.3}$$

Further studies on more complicated atoms than hydrogen showed that the spectral lines emitted from these could also be represented by somewhat similar expressions, although the integers themselves had to be replaced by an integer plus a constant parameter. In other words the general expression for the wave-number of lines emitted from atoms could be written in the form

$$\bar{v} = RZ^2\left[\frac{1}{(n_1+\alpha)^2} - \frac{1}{(n_2+\beta)^2}\right] \tag{4.4}$$

where α and β were constants which retained the same value for the different spectral lines of a given series but varied in value from one series of lines to the other. However, the fundamental multiplying constant R remains the same for all these different series of spectral lines, which was the crucial point that came from the studies of Rydberg and Ritz, and it was for this reason that the constant R came to be known as the Rydberg constant.

Hence in 1910 a large number of experimental observations on spectral lines were available, and the first step in the application of any scientific method had been taken in that these observations had been correlated together and definite relationships between them established. However, at this time there was no understanding whatever of the reasons for the particular expressions, nor indeed why spectral lines, constituting single frequencies, were emitted from atoms in the first place. It was against this kind of background that the new model of the atom proposed by Rutherford was set, and any atomic model proposed at this time would obviously be expected to give some kind of explanation for the existence of spectral lines, and hopefully some reason for the particular expressions determining their wavenumbers.

The classical theory of radiation could indeed be applied to the Rutherford atom, and at first sight it would appear that this gives a very satisfactory explanation of the emission of radiation in the visible region. Thus comparison can be made with the radiation produced in the r.f. region of the spectrum by the pulses of current oscillating up and down a dipole aerial which is connected to a radio transmitter. Such an aerial is shown in Fig. 4.3, and the successive positions of the current pulse are indicated, together with the way in which loops of electric and magnetic fields are produced from it: these radiate out from the aerial and constitute the outgoing electromagnetic radiation. In the case of shorter radio-waves the aerial will be of the order of 1 m in length, and the frequency of the oscillations of the order of 100 MHz. The same basic principle can, however, be scaled down by many orders of magnitude and applied to the motion of an electron around an atomic nucleus.

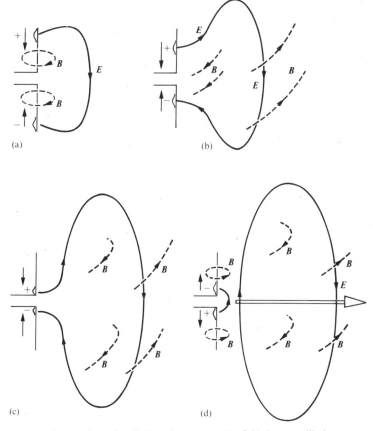

FIG. 4.3. Production of radiating electromagnetic field from oscillating current pulses in a dipole aerial.

Thus if the orbit of such an electron around the Rutherford atom is viewed edge on, the single electron will appear to be moving in a vertical line and executing oscillations of exactly the same nature as those of the current pulses in a radio-aerial. The length of such an effective aerial will now only be that of the diameter of the atom, but the same principles for the emission of electromagnetic radiation should apply on the classical theory, and the frequency of the emitted radiation will then be determined by the rate of rotation of the electron about the nucleus, and a calculation of this for the hydrogen atom will give a frequency of about $6 \cdot 6 \times 10^{15}$ Hz.

This frequency is indeed of just the magnitude required for radiation in the u.v. or optical region, and it would therefore appear that the Rutherford atom will give a very satisfactory account of the emission of visible light from atoms. A major difficulty arises, however, when the exact frequency of this radiation is calculated and it becomes apparent that this frequency will in fact change continuously as the electron loses energy to the electromagnetic radiation and spirals in towards the nucleus. The period of oscillation of the electron around the atom will then also change, and hence as the electron continues to radiate, its period of rotation around the nucleus will become shorter as it spirals in towards the centre. Thus the spectra observed should be in the form of a radiation pattern smeared across the whole of the visible region instead of a set of single precise frequencies. Hence the very existence of the discrete spectral lines themselves seems to be contradicted by the Rutherford model since the energy loss during emission of electromagnetic radiation implies that there should be a continuous change in emitted frequency. Thus the Rutherford model which had been so successful in explaining the scattering experiments now seemed to be doomed by its inability to explain the existence of spectral lines, and it was against this particular background that Bohr came forward with his proposals which linked the quantum concepts of radiation directly to the new model of atomic structure that was now available.

Bohr's postulates

Bohr was able to save the model of the Rutherford atom by taking the quantum concepts which had been established by Planck and Einstein for the nature of radiation, and, by applying these same concepts to quantization within the atomic orbitals, suggest an actual mechanism whereby the absorption and emission of quantized packets of radiation could occur. It should be stressed at the outset, however, that Bohr's theory is very much a mixture of the older classical approach together with the newer quantum concepts. It is extremely inconsistent in its treatment, since classical mechanics are applied to the orbiting electron, although the postulates which are then added contradict all the basic ideas of classical physics which had been previously accepted. Moreover there is no justification whatever for the three postulates which Bohr puts forward, apart from the fact that they produce the right answer. In fact it was not until twelve years later that any real justification for these postulates could be provided.

Hence one could reject Bohr's theory and take the view that it is such a mixture of old classical ideas, together with unjustified quantum concepts, that it is far better forgotten and the modern wave-mechanical model of the atom considered immediately. It can be argued, however, that the very way in which our present concept of the atom has been obtained via the Bohr model is an important lesson in itself, since, in the history of physics and science in general, the full and correct answer is hardly ever reached in one step, and partial or half-true models are often a necessary intermediate. There is also no doubt that Bohr's theory played an absolutely crucial part in the history of atomic physics, since it was the first attempt to apply the new ideas of quantized radiation and energy to the structure of matter.

The three postulates which Bohr proposed should be applied to the hydrogen atom, in order to explain the emission of spectral lines were as follows:

(i) Electrons can only rotate in certain orbits which have a specified radius and cannot move into orbits which lie between these. (This first postulate contradicts the basic ideas of classical mechanics since an electron rotating in an orbit is an accelerating electric charge, which on classical electromagnetism must radiate energy, and in doing so must spiral in towards the nucleus, hence moving into an orbit of smaller radius.)

(ii) The allowed orbits are given by the condition that the angular momentum of the electron is quantized and equal to $n \times h/2\pi$. (Again there was at the time no reason or justification for this statement.)

(iii) Emission or absorption of radiation occurs when an electron jumps from one allowed orbit to another, and the frequency of such radiation is then given by the expression

$$h\nu = E_2 - E_1. \tag{4.5}$$

(This proposes a mechanism for the emission of electromagnetic radiation which has no justification nor conceptual model in classical physics.)

Although all of the above postulates contradict the concepts of classical physics and have no *a priori* justification, it will be clear that Bohr was attempting to apply the idea that energy could only change in discrete amounts, rather than continuously, to the energy states of the atom itself as well as to the radiation which was emitted by it.

The semi-classical–quantum approach

The way in which Bohr combined his three postulates with an ordinary classical calculation of the energy states of the atom in which a single electron of charge $-e$ is visualized as rotating around a positive nucleus of charge $+Ze$, can be summarized as follows:

If r is the radius of the orbit and v is the velocity of the electron, the equation for motion in a circle may be written

$$\frac{mv^2}{r} = \frac{Ze \cdot e}{r^2} \cdot \frac{1}{4\pi\varepsilon_0} \tag{4.6}$$

where the right-hand side represents the electrostatic force between the electron and the nucleus.

This may be rewritten in either of the forms

$$mvr = \frac{Ze^2}{v} \cdot \frac{1}{4\pi\varepsilon_0} \tag{4.7}$$

or

$$\tfrac{1}{2}mv^2 = \frac{Ze^2}{2r} \cdot \frac{1}{4\pi\varepsilon_0}. \tag{4.8}$$

Potential energy of the electron

It is clear that the object of the calculation is to obtain an expression for the total energy of the electron, and this will be partially kinetic (and given by $\tfrac{1}{2}mv^2$) and partially potential. However before an expression can be quoted for the value of the potential energy the zero reference point must be defined. In principle this could be chosen at any arbitrary point, e.g. at the nucleus, at a distance of 10^{-10} m from the nucleus, or any other distance. Energy *differences*, which are all that need to be calculated in the end, would always be the same whatever the reference point was, provided the same reference was always used. In practice it is mathematically more convenient to chose a zero reference as r equals infinity, i.e. when the electron is completely removed from the nucleus.

Since the electron *loses* potential energy as it is attracted in towards the nucleus, and the work done *by* the electron in moving from infinity to a specific distance r_1 is given by

$$\int_{r_1}^{\infty} \frac{Ze^2}{4\pi\varepsilon_0 r^2} \cdot \mathrm{d}r = -\frac{Ze^2}{r_1} \cdot \frac{1}{4\pi\varepsilon_0},$$

it follows that the potential energy of the electron at a distance r_1 will be

$$V = -\frac{Ze^2}{r_1} \cdot \frac{1}{4\pi\varepsilon_0}. \tag{4.9}$$

It should again be stressed, however, that the negative sign only arises because of the particular choice of the zero reference point and has no other implication.

It now follows that the total energy of the electron will be given by

$$E = \tfrac{1}{2}mv^2 - \frac{Ze^2}{r_1} \cdot \frac{1}{4\pi\varepsilon_0} \tag{4.10}$$

which can be combined with eqn (4.8) to give

$$E = -\tfrac{1}{2}mv^2. \tag{4.11}$$

The quantization of angular momentum

Bohr's second postulate may now be applied to determine which orbits are allowed. The quantization of the angular momentum (mvr) of the electron can be represented by

$$mvr = n\frac{h}{2\pi} \tag{4.12}$$

where n is an integer. This may now be combined with eqn (4.7) to give

$$v = \frac{Ze^2}{4\pi\varepsilon_0} \cdot \frac{2\pi}{nh}. \tag{4.13}$$

This expression for v may then be substituted into eqn (4.11) to give the final expression for the energy of the quantized orbit, for a given value of n as

$$E_n = -\tfrac{1}{2}m\left[\frac{Ze^2}{2\varepsilon_0} \cdot \frac{1}{nh}\right]^2$$

$$= -\frac{mZ^2e^4}{8\varepsilon_0^2 h^2} \cdot \frac{1}{n^2}. \tag{4.14}$$

Bohr's final postulate which defines the frequency of the absorbed and emitted radiation can then be written in the form

$$h\nu = E_{n_2} - E_{n_1}$$

$$\text{i.e.} \quad h\nu = \frac{mZ^2e^4}{8\varepsilon_0^2 h^2}\left[\frac{1}{n_1^2} - \frac{1}{n_2^2}\right]$$

or, in terms of wave numbers

$$\bar{\nu} = \frac{\nu}{c} = \frac{mZ^2e^4}{8\varepsilon_0^2 h^3 c}\left[\frac{1}{n_1^2} - \frac{1}{n_2^2}\right]. \tag{4.15}$$

The Bohr theory and spectral lines

It is clear that the three Bohr postulates will produce atomic spectral lines rather than a smeared out continuum, since the existence of quantized energy states, and transitions between them, are essential concepts behind the postulates. The great triumph of the Bohr theory, however, was the fact that it correctly predicted the form of the quantitative expressions for the frequency of the spectral lines and even predicted the magnitude of the constants involved, to high accuracy. Thus it is clear that the general nature of the expressions for the Balmer, Lyman, and other series of lines in atomic hydrogen is explained by the two terms at the end of eqn (4.15) and the difference between the inverses of the squared integers arises as a characteristic feature of the Bohr theory. The really convincing evidence in favour of the Bohr theory came from the fact that the constant predicted in eqn (4.15) was accurately equal to the Rydberg constant as measured empirically for the hydrogen atom. Thus substitution of values for the charge and mass of the electron and the Planck constant in eqn (4.15), give a value of the Rydberg constant predicted by Bohr's theory of $1\cdot0974 \times 10^7$ m^{-1}, whereas the value which had been obtained from spectroscopic measurements was $1\cdot0968 \times 10^7$ m^{-1}. It was clear that such remarkable agreement between theory and experiment could hardly be fortuitous. Although the conceptual basis of the Bohr theory is very mixed, there could be no doubt that in some way it was reflecting a correct picture, the elucidation of which awaited the concept of stationary electron waves some twelve years later.

It is clear that the essential contribution of the Bohr theory has been to provide a picture of the atom in which certain well specified electron orbits can be regarded as having distinct energies associated with them. The process of radiation absorption or emission is correlated with the electron jumps between these precise energy levels. The model can thus be represented diagrammatically as in Fig. 4.4(a), where the electron transitions are shown

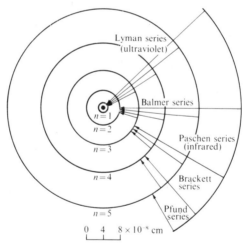

Fig. 4.4. Energy level transitions in atomic hydrogen. (a) Between atomic orbitals. (b) On a term diagram.

taking place between a series of circular concentric electron orbits, or alternatively by the simple energy level diagram of Fig. 4.4(b), where the energy of successive orbits is plotted on a vertical scale with that of the innermost orbit shown at the bottom. It will be noticed that the energy has been plotted on a scale with a zero at the top, and the axis extending negatively downwards,

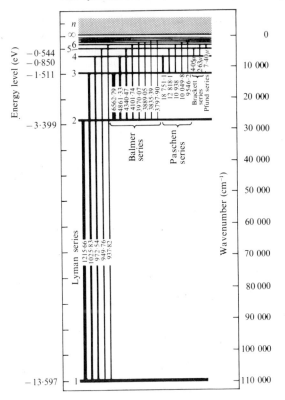

F\scriptsize IG. 4.4(b).

because the zero of potential energy was chosen when the electron was at an infinite distance from the nucleus, and as a result of this all the energy values of the different orbits have a negative sign, and are in fact obtained by plotting $-R/n^2$, where n ranges from 1 to ∞. It also becomes clear from such an energy-level diagram, how the series limit arises for each set of spectral lines, since when n approaches infinity the energy of the electron will be zero, and the largest energy and frequency associated with a given series of spectral lines will thus be simply determined by the magnitude of the first term in the series (i.e. $R/1^2$ for the Lyman series, $R/2^2$ for the Balmer series etc.).

This energy-level diagram for the hydrogen atom is of a very simple form, and all the observed spectral lines can, to a first approximation, be explained simply by different transitions between these sets of levels. When more complicated atoms are considered, however, such an energy-level diagram, or term diagram, as it is often called, becomes much more complex. This essentially arises because the presence of other electrons around the nucleus alters the expression for the energy of the single electron under consideration. The expression then depends not only on the single quantum number, n, but also on another quantum number, l, the full significance of which awaited the advent of the wave-mechanical model of atomic orbitals, as described at the end of the next chapter.

PROBLEMS

4.1. Calculate the wavelengths of the Paschen Series of lines from atomic hydrogen.

4.2. Derive expressions for the tangential and angular velocities of an electron in a Bohr orbit of an atom of atomic number Z in terms of the electronic charge, rest mass, the principal quantum number n, and h and ε_0. Calculate the values of these velocities for the smallest orbit of atomic hydrogen.

4.3. Calculate the maximum velocity of the electrons emitted from the metal surface of a photo-cell of work function 3·6 eV when it is illuminated with light from a hydrogen lamp having a quartz window which will pass all optical and u.v. wavelengths.

4.4. Given that the value of the Rydberg constant is $1·1 \times 10^7$ m^{-1} calculate which of the Balmer series of atomic transitions has enough energy to release electrons from a metal surface of work-function 2·6 eV.

4.5. Given that the momentum of a photon is equal to $h\nu/c$, calculate the recoil velocity of a hydrogen atom, which is initially at rest in free space, when it emits radiation corresponding to the first transition of the Lyman series.

4.6. Positronium is formed when an electron and a positron are transiently held in a system in which each revolves around their common centre of mass. Apply the general approach of the Bohr method to this system, deriving an expression for its energy levels, and calculating the wavelength of the $n = 2$ to $n = 1$ transition.

4.7. Apply the Bohr theory to the singly ionized helium atom, and predict the wavelengths of the spectral lines arising from transitions from the four lowest excited states of the ground state.

4.8. In the simple Bohr theory the nucleus is assumed to be at rest while the electron rotates around it. In fact they both revolve about their common centre of gravity. It can be shown that all the expressions derived on the Bohr theory still hold if the electron mass m_e is replaced by a 'reduced mass' μ which is equal to $m_e M_N/(m_e + M_N)$ where M_N is the mass of the nucleus. Justify this statement and calculate the percentage correction that it gives to the predicted spectral line frequencies for (i) atomic hydrogen, (ii) doubly ionized lithium which has a nuclear mass of 7 atomic mass units.

4.9. High resolution studies of the yellow line of wavelength 5 890 Å from atomic sodium show that this line consists of a doublet. This doublet is attributed to the interaction between the magnetic moments of the electron spin and its orbital motion. If the strength of this interaction produces a splitting of 1 700 m^{-1} in the upper energy level calculate (i) the ratio of the wavelength separation of the doublet to the wavelength of the emission line, and (ii) the effective magnetic field acting on the electron spin, using the data given in Problem 1.12.

5. The quantum model—X-ray scattering

Compton's experiments

THE previous work of Einstein on the photoelectric effect and of Bohr on the Rutherford atom, had established the model of radiation as consisting of discrete quanta, or wave packets, each with an energy $h\nu$. These were still visualized essentially as packets of waves, and in this sense quite distinct from particles. The experiments which were undertaken by A. H. Compton in 1923, however, showed that such a clear cut difference did not, in fact, exist, and that to some extent the wave packets had to be considered like particles, possessing particle-like properties and in particular linear momentum.

Compton's experiments were concerned with the scattering of X-rays of a well-defined wavelength, λ_0, by a thin film of metallic foil. The angle through which the X-rays have been scattered is found by measuring their angular distribution on the far side of the foil. Compton not only measured the angles through which the scattering occurred, but also the wavelength of the scattered radiation. A typical set of results, as taken from his original paper of 1923, is shown in Fig. 5.1. The different curves from left to right indicate the vari-

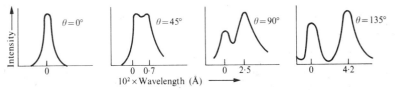

FIG. 5.1. Results of Compton's X-ray scattering experiments. θ is the angle of scatter. Horizontal axis gives change in wavelength for scattered component.

ation of intensity with wavelength of the scattered radiation, for four different angles of scattering. Thus the first curve on the left gives the result for direct transmission through the metal foil with no scattering at all, and in this case it is seen that all the radiation is still centred around the original wavelength λ_0. However, as the angle of scatter is increased through 45°, 90°, to 135°, an additional wavelength component comes into the intensity variation. It can be seen that for each angle of scattering, the intensity is concentrated around two wavelengths, i.e. some at the original wavelength λ_0, while the rest is centred around a new wavelength, λ_1, which varies with the angle of scatter. It is clear that the wavelength of this new component is always greater than that of the incident radiation, and that it increases with increasing angle of scatter. Alternatively, in terms of frequency, the frequency of the scattered radiation is always less than that of the incident radiation, and decreases continuously with the increase in angle of scatter.

The very existence of a component of radiation with a different frequency from that of the incident waves, was quite contrary to any picture of the radiation as composed of waves, or series of waves. One of the crucial properties of wave-motion is that its frequency is determined by the emitting source, as can be readily visualized either from the waves produced on a ripple tank from a dipping mechanical finger, or the waves produced from an atom by an energy jump, since in both cases the property of the source itself (the mechanical motion of the finger in one case, and the difference in energy between the two levels in the other) is the factor which determines the frequency v. Although waves can be reflected, refracted, diffracted, and caused to interfere, none of these processes can change the frequency of radiation (nor its wavelength if measurements are always carried out in the same medium). Hence the very existence of Compton's measurements indicates that the concept of radiation as wave-motion cannot be complete. Moreover, the consideration of the way in which the energy of the scattered radiation varied with angle, suggested to Compton that this was qualitatively very similar to the angular dependence that would be expected for a particle which had been in collision with another particle to produce elastic scattering. He therefore proposed that it might be possible to treat the scattering process as a collision between two particles, but in order to follow this through, some expression for the momentum of the 'wave-particle' had to be derived.

Wave packets with momentum

In order to determine the amount of linear momentum that should be associated with such a localized wave packet, two expressions which had been developed from the general theory of relativity need to be used. One of these describes the well-known fact that the mass of a particle increases with its speed, and the quantitative relation is given by

$$m = m_0/(1 - v^2/c^2)^{\frac{1}{2}}, \tag{5.1}$$

and the other expression gives the total energy of the particle with momentum p and rest mass m_0, which is

$$E^2 = c^2 p^2 + (m_0 c^2)^2. \tag{5.2}$$

It is evident that the quantum of radiation has some rather specialized properties when compared with other particles. It travels at the velocity of light c, and hence it follows from eqn (5.1) that m_0, its rest mass, must be zero, since otherwise it would have an infinite mass, and hence an infinite energy, as it moved through space. The magnitude of the momentum that should be associated with it, can therefore be best calculated by applying eqn (5.2). If $m_0 = 0$ is substituted into this, the equation reduces to

$$E = cp \quad \text{i.e.} \quad p = E/c = h\nu/c = \frac{h}{\lambda}. \tag{5.3}$$

It may be noted that this same expression can be derived more quickly by steps which are, however, difficult to justify conceptually. The total energy of a particle can be written as mc^2, and if the concept of momentum as equal to mass × velocity is interpreted as $m \times c$ in this case, it then follows directly that

$$E = (mc) \times c = p \times c.$$

Therefore

$$p = \frac{E}{c} = \frac{h}{\lambda}.$$

Another point of interest is that the classical theory of electromagnetic radiation does predict a momentum content per unit volume of such radiation, and this can be shown to be equal to E/c where E represents the energy content per unit volume. Thus the basic form of the expression is the same in both cases, but the concept of the momentum as concentrated in a wave packet, or particle, is of course completely absent from the classical theory. Compton's scattering experiments may now be analysed in terms of the collision between two particles, i.e. the incident X-ray quantum with a momentum h/λ_0, and one of the electrons which may be in the outer orbit of an atom or one of the conduction electrons in the metallic foil. Since the energies involved in the process are very much greater than those binding the electron to the atom, it may be assumed to a good approximation that the electron is in fact at rest, and hence its momentum before the scattering process can be taken as zero. The analysis of the Compton scattering is then carried through by applying the two conservation laws of energy and linear momentum to this collision process and evaluating the change in momentum, and hence of wavelength, for the scattered quantum.

Conservation laws and the scattering process

The scattering of an individual X-ray quantum by a single electron is illustrated diagrammatically in Fig. 5.2, and an incident quantum is shown with a wavelength λ_0 and thus an initial momentum h/λ_0. After being scattered through an angle θ it is shown with a wavelength λ_1 and hence a momentum h/λ_1. The principle of the conservation of momentum can therefore be applied to this collision, by resolving the momentum along the original direction of the X-ray quantum, and then at right angles to this, and in both cases equating

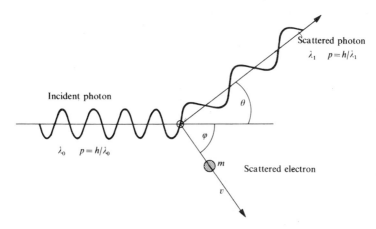

FIG. 5.2. Collision process in Compton scattering.

the momentum before impact with that after impact. These equations then become

<table>
<tr><td></td><td>Momentum before
impact</td><td>Momentum after
impact</td></tr>
<tr><td>Along direction of λ_0</td><td>$\dfrac{h}{\lambda_0}$</td><td>$= \dfrac{h}{\lambda_1} \cos \theta + mv \cos \phi$ (5.4)</td></tr>
<tr><td>Perpendicular direction</td><td>0</td><td>$= \dfrac{h}{\lambda_1} \sin \theta - mv \sin \phi$ (5.5)</td></tr>
</table>

Hence

$$\left(\frac{h}{\lambda_0} - \frac{h}{\lambda_1} \cos \theta \right) = mv \cos \phi,$$

$$\frac{h}{\lambda_1} \sin \theta = mv \sin \phi.$$

The angle ϕ, which is impossible to measure in any simple way, may then be eliminated by squaring and adding these two equations to give

$$\frac{h^2}{\lambda_0^2} - \frac{2h^2}{\lambda_0 \lambda_1} \cos \theta + \frac{h^2}{\lambda_1^2} = m^2 v^2. \tag{5.6}$$

Another relation may be found by applying the principle of the conservation of energy and equating the energy before impact to that afterwards, bearing in mind that the stationary electron has a rest energy of $m_0 c^2$, and that the energy of the quantum equals $h\nu$, and hence $\dfrac{hc}{\lambda}$. Hence

$$\frac{hc}{\lambda_0} + m_0 c^2 = \frac{hc}{\lambda_1} + mc^2. \tag{5.7}$$

$$\therefore \quad \frac{h}{\lambda_0} - \frac{h}{\lambda_1} + m_0 c = mc. \tag{5.8}$$

The value for m, the mass of the electron when travelling with velocity v, has already been given in eqn (5.1). This may be rewritten as

$$m^2 v^2 = m^2 c^2 - m_0^2 c^2. \tag{5.9}$$

Substitution of $m^2 c^2$ into this expression from eqn (5.8) then gives

$$m^2 v^2 = \left(\frac{h}{\lambda_0} - \frac{h}{\lambda_1} + m_0 c \right)^2 - m_0^2 c^2. \tag{5.10}$$

The expression $m^2 v^2$ may now be eliminated between this equation and eqn (5.6) to give

$$\frac{2h^2}{\lambda_0 \lambda_1} \cos \theta = \frac{2h^2}{\lambda_0 \lambda_1} + 2m_0 c \left(\frac{h}{\lambda_1} - \frac{h}{\lambda_0} \right).$$

Multiplying through by $\lambda_0 \lambda_1 / 2hm_0 c$ then gives

$$\Delta \lambda = \lambda_1 - \lambda_0 = \frac{h}{m_0 c} (1 - \cos \theta). \tag{5.11}$$

This expression thus predicts that the change in wavelength produced by the scattering will vary as $(1 - \cos \theta)$, as was found to be the case experimentally, and also, somewhat surprisingly, is independent of the initial wavelength λ_0. Compton's measurements not only confirmed the quantitative angular variation, but also the value of the scattering constant $h/m_0 c$ which is equal to $2 \cdot 4 \times 10^{-12}$ m, or $0 \cdot 024$ Å, and is usually referred to as 'the Compton wavelength of the electron'.

The component of the scattered radiation seen in the curves of Fig. 5.1 which retains the original wavelength λ_0, arises from quanta which are scattered by the nucleus, or atom as a whole, instead of one of the outer electrons. For such a case the m_0 in (eqn 5.11) will be replaced by the nuclear mass, and hence the change in wavelength will be negligible.

The particle-like nature of radiation

It will be evident that the work of Compton established the concept of the particle-like nature of radiation in a much more definite way even than the wave packets proposed by Einstein to explain the photoelectric effect. Thus the wave packets of the photoelectric effect introduced the idea of a localization in space and time for the quanta of radiation since they could cause the ejection of a photoelectron from a specific point on a metallic surface at a given instant of time. The idea that momentum could also be associated with this localized wave packet awaited Compton's work, however, and the effect of this associated momentum becomes more apparent the higher the energy of the quantum of radiation.

At the lower-frequency end of the electromagnetic spectrum, in the radio- and microwave regions, radiation is normally treated as a classical wave-motion, and most of the problems are concerned with phenomena such as reflection or refraction of the waves. However, even in this low-frequency and low-energy region, it is still possible to demonstrate the quantized nature of radiation. Recently various types of radio-frequency and microwave spectroscopy have been developed, in which the individual quanta of radiation at these frequencies interact with the specific energy levels within either molecules or solids to produce transitions between them, as is considered in detail in Chapter 6. The momentum associated with such quanta is extremely small, however, and hence these particle-like properties are not normally demonstrable in the low-frequency regions.

The wave-like nature of particles *matter*

One of the most brilliant deductions of modern physics followed the work of Compton when, in 1924, Louis de Broglie made the suggestion that if radiation had a particle-like nature, then it should follow from basic concepts of symmetry that particles ought to possess a wave-like nature of some kind. Moreover he went on to suggest that the same basic relationship should exist in the two cases, and thus the waves to be associated with particles ought to be related to their momentum by the same relation as eqn (5.3). For the specific case of an electron the wave length associated with it should be given by

$$\lambda = \frac{h}{mv} \tag{5.12}$$

where m is the mass of the electron and v its velocity.

De Broglie made this suggestion in his Ph.D. thesis at the University of Paris and was nearly failed for putting forward such an unlikely idea. Einstein was passing through Paris that weekend and the thesis was referred to him for comment. It was only because Einstein suggested there might conceivably be something in the proposition that de Broglie was awarded his doctorate for what later turned out to be one of the most brilliant concepts of the century.

If de Broglie's suggestion is correct, the wavelength to be associated with an electron after it has been accelerated through say 100 volts, can easily be calculated. Thus its velocity will be given by $\frac{1}{2}mv^2 = eV$ and the resultant wavelength will therefore be given

$$\lambda = \frac{h}{mv} = \frac{h}{\sqrt{(2meV)}} = 1{\cdot}226 \times 10^{-10} \text{ m} = 1{\cdot}226 \text{ Å}.$$

Such wavelengths are therefore of the same order of magnitude as those of X-rays, and it should thus be possible to use the same experimental means to demonstrate the existence of matter waves as had been used to demonstrate the wave nature of X-rays. It would therefore appear that the regular array of atoms in a crystal, which have a spacing of several ångströms between them, might well provide a convenient diffraction grating for electron waves as they had previously for X-rays. Experiments on the scattering of electron beams by the atoms at the surface of the crystal, which were being undertaken by Davisson and Germer, were in fact the first experimental proof of the existence of these waves, although Davisson and Germer had started these series of experiments before realizing this possibility.

A diagrammatic outline of their apparatus is shown in Fig. 5.3. It is seen

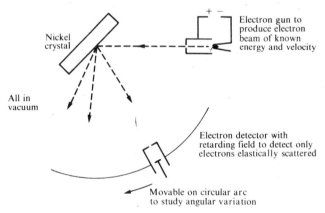

FIG. 5.3. Davisson and Germer experiment on electron diffraction—in diagrammatic form.

that a beam of electrons is directed onto the surface of a nickel crystal. The electrons which have been elastically scattered from this and still retain the same energy are picked up by a detector which can be moved round in the arc of a circle. Thus the angular variation of the scattering can be measured. In their initial studies an unannealed nickel surface was employed and a smeared out pattern was obtained for the electron scattering as shown in Fig. 5.4(a) which is taken from their original paper. However, in the course of their experiment, the vacuum system accidentally broke and the nickel

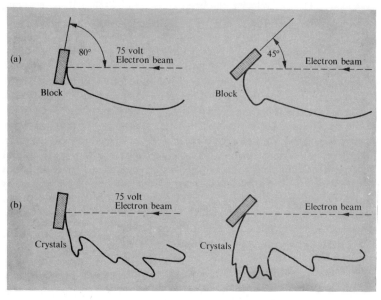

FIG. 5.4. Results of Davisson and Germer electron scattering experiment (a) before annealing the nickel surface, (b) after annealing nickel surface.

surface which was then at a fairly high temperature became badly oxidized. In order to remove the oxide layer they annealed the nickel surface in a high-temperature oven and then repeated the experiments. The electron scattering was then found to have very pronounced maxima and minima as shown in Fig. 5.4(b).

It is clear that any systematic variation in intensity of this pattern must indicate interference phenomena: the maxima in the pattern define the directions in which the waves scattered by successive crystal layers are in phase with one another and add up constructively, while the minima indicate the directions in which they are exactly π out of phase with each other and cancel. The conditions for such maxima are therefore identical to those which were derived earlier by the Braggs for the case of X-ray diffraction. A study of Fig. 5.5 will indicate that the path-length difference for rays which have been scattered from successive layers of crystals is given by $2d \sin \theta$, and hence the condition for maxima to occur in the scattering pattern will be

$$n\lambda = 2d \sin \theta \tag{5.13}$$

where n is an integer, d is the atomic spacing, and λ the wavelength of the incident radiation. This equation was used by Bragg, when initiating the study

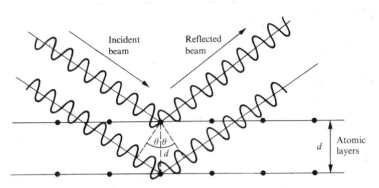

Condition for constructive interference is that
the path difference of $2d \sin\theta$ should be equal
to an integral number of wavelengths $n\lambda$

FIG. 5.5. Condition for constructive interference for X-rays or electrons reflected from successive atomic layers.

of X-ray crystallography, to determine the wavelength of X-rays in the first place and then, once λ was known, to evaluate the interatomic spacings within crystals and hence the detailed structure of the crystals themselves.

Exactly the same relationship can be applied to the scattering of the electrons by the crystal lattice, if they do indeed have some wave property associated with them. Davisson and Germer therefore proceeded to analyse their results in terms of the Bragg equation and hence deduce the wavelength of the electrons, since the spacing of the nickel atoms was already known. The value thus obtained for the wavelengths of the electrons was 1·65 Å, and this experimentally determined wavelength could then be compared with that predicted theoretically by the de Broglie relationship. The momentum of the electrons could readily be calculated from the accelerating voltage of 54 volts which had been used to produce the beam, and substitution of these values into eqn (5.12) then gave the value of 1·67 Å. This very good agreement between the predicted and experimentally measured value for the first set of electron diffraction curves that were obtained was striking evidence for the truth of de Broglie's suggestion. It was quickly confirmed by experiments by G. P. Thomson at Cambridge. He directed a collimated beam of higher-energy electrons through a very thin sheet of metal and studied the diffraction patterns that were then obtained on the far side. Thus by the end of 1924 there was extremely convincing evidence that not only did waves behave like particles, and this could be readily demonstrated for high-energy radiation, but also particles, such as electrons, often exhibited wave-like properties. In both cases the fundamental equation relating the wavelength and linear momentum could be written in the form $\lambda = \dfrac{h}{P}$.

Wave packets and the uncertainty principle

It is clear that the idea of wave packets can now be associated with both quanta of radiation and with particles of matter, such as the electron. Such wave packets must be formed out of more than a single monochromatic wavelength, however, since a single wavelength or frequency would produce a perfect sinusoidal wave pattern extending to infinity in both directions. If a mathematical analysis, known as Fourier analysis, is applied to a wave packet such as that shown in Fig. 5.6, it can be broken down into a sum of waves of slightly different wavelength and frequency, with values centred on that given by de Broglie's relation, but spreading a measurable amount to each side. Moreover the tighter the bunching of the wave packet the wider will be the spread of frequencies and wavelengths in its components, as shown by the two examples in Fig. 5.6.

The fact that this is so can be readily shown mathematically for the slightly simpler case of two component waves. Thus, in general terms, two waves of slightly different frequency and wavelength can be written as

$$\psi_1 = a \cos 2\pi(v_1 t - k_1 x)$$

and

$$\psi_2 = a \cos 2\pi(v_2 t - k_2 x) \tag{5.14}$$

where $\Delta v = v_1 - v_2$ and k is equal to $\dfrac{1}{\lambda}$ so that $\Delta k = \dfrac{1}{\lambda_1} - \dfrac{1}{\lambda_2}$.

Addition of these two waves then gives a resultant

$$\psi_{(1+2)} = 2a \cos 2\pi\left[\frac{v_1 + v_1}{2}t - \frac{k_1 + k_2}{2}x\right]\cos 2\pi\left[\frac{v_1 - v_2}{2}t - \frac{k_1 - k_2}{2}x\right]. \tag{5.15}$$

This resultant represents a carrier wave of the average frequency and wavelength of the two original waves, but modulated by a lower-frequency longer-wavelength group, with wavelength equal to $2/(k_1 - k_2)$. Hence a half-wavelength, which is the length of one 'wave group' or 'packet' as indicated in Fig. 5.6(c) is equal to $1/\Delta k$.

If we are dealing with electron waves, $k = 1/\lambda = p/h$ and hence the length of one group or packet will be given by $h/\Delta p$. This distance, however, is also the 'uncertainty in position' of the wave packet or electron which it represents, and hence can be equated to Δx when applied to particle motion. It therefore follows that

$$\Delta x = h/\Delta p, \quad \therefore \quad \Delta x . \Delta p = h. \tag{5.16}$$

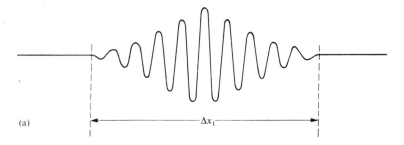

(a)

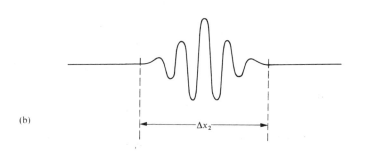

(b)

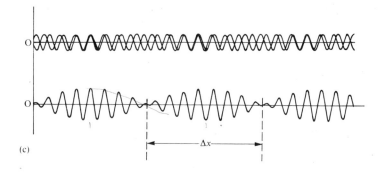

(c)

FIG. 5.6. Wave packets and their properties. (a) Wave packet with large width requires little spread of wavelengths in components. (b) Wave packet with small width requires large spread of wavelengths in components. (c) Summation of two waves of slightly different wavelengths produces a series of wave groups or packets. Outer groups are nullified if summation is taken over a *range* of wavelengths—leaving only central group.

This equation has been derived assuming that only two component waves contribute to the wave packet whereas it is in fact made up of a whole series of components with frequencies varying from v_1 to v_2 and wavenumbers from k_1 to k_2. If a full mathematical analysis of this more general case is carried through, it is found first that the condition then becomes

$$\Delta x . \Delta p = h/2\pi, \tag{5.17}$$

and secondly that only *one* wave group or packet results from the summation of all the different components, since these will nullify each other at all distances removed more than half a wavelength from the centre of the group, which is, by definition, the one point at which they are all in phase. It follows that the summation of component waves covering a range of frequencies and wavelengths is the accurate description of the travelling electron, since only one wave group then exists to specify its position. This can then be specified to an accuracy such that

$$\Delta x = \frac{h}{2\pi} . \frac{1}{\Delta p}. \tag{5.18}$$

Although the expression has actually been derived by considering the motion of an electron, it could have been obtained equally well by considering the motion of a photon. A quantum of radiation of frequency v, with energy hv, will have a momentum hv/c and, since exactly the same relation holds between its wavelength and momentum as does for the electron, it follows that the wave packet of the quantum will also be governed by eqn (5.17) and (5.18).

These equations are, in fact, a statement of a very fundamental concept in physics called the Uncertainty Principle and apply to both matter and energy in all their forms. This principle implies that precise simultaneous measurement of both position and momentum of any individual particle, such as an electron or photon, is impossible. There must always be some uncertainty or imprecision in such measurements and the product of these uncertainties will be equal to $h/2\pi$.

The applications of the uncertainty principle are very far-ranging, from its philosophical implications for a rigid deterministic view of the Universe to its very practical predictions. One of these is the fact that helium will not solidify under ordinary atmospheric pressure, however low the temperature, because if it did the positions and momenta of the individual atoms would then be known too precisely.

An alternative form of stating the uncertainty principle is in terms of the measurement of the energy of the system and the time taken for the measurement. The corresponding relation then becomes

$$\Delta E . \Delta t = h/2\pi. \tag{5.19}$$

One of the immediate practical applications of this is to predict a 'natural' line width for any spectral line, which will exist simply because of the limited time the atom spends in its excited state. Other applications and implications of the uncertainty principle will be met in later sections of the book, and it is one of the basic concepts underlying physical theory.

Complementary models or irresolvable paradox

It will be seen in a later section that the association of waves with electrons answers some of the dilemmas that had been arising in the development of atomic physics. In particular it justifies Bohr's concept of stationary orbits, since these can be shown to have a circumference which will just include an integral number of wavelengths, and hence support a stationary wave pattern which in turn can store energy. The introduction of the idea that waves can be associated with particles does, however, introduce its own conceptual difficulties. It is now not clear, either in the case of radiation, or in the case of particles such as electrons, whether the 'correct' picture is one of waves or of particles. It would appear to be very difficult to maintain that they were both particles and waves at one and the same time, with the different properties that would normally be associated with these. Yet it becomes clear that under certain conditions they do behave like waves, while under other conditions they behave like particles.

The dilemma may be best stated by suggesting that there are four different theories that could be put forward to resolve this difficulty. Each of these four theories can then be briefly analysed in turn. These four theories might be summarized as:

(a) the waves and particles are both real;
(b) the waves are real and the particles are illusory;
(c) the particles are real and the waves are illusory;
(d) the waves and particles are both to some extent illusory (i.e. neither are perfect representations or analogies).

It would seem that any consistent approach must reject the first possibility (a) since this involves a 'blind eye' theory in which one set of evidence is specifically ignored while the other is accepted. At first sight the second theory (b) has a good deal to commend it, especially if the concept of the wave packet, or wave group, with a definite localization in space, is developed. However, if an electron is only to be described physically by a wave concept and the idea of a particle entity is entirely eliminated, the effect on an electron beam as it passes through different potential regions is impossible to explain. A wave treatment of propagation across the boundary between two regions shows that the waves will be split into two. Both reflection and refraction will occur at such a potential boundary, as takes place when visible light for instance moves from air into glass. Such effects do not take place for the electron beam, however, and the individual electrons pass on through the potential boundary. Although their motion is significantly altered, their identity is not removed. In other words their particle-like nature is more 'real' than can be represented by a group of waves alone.

Turning now to theory (c), it might appear that this really provides the best solution to 'the dilemma. Examples of illusory waves, which are nevertheless extremely useful in analysing problems, may be quoted from the macroscopic world, such as a 'crime wave', which can be visualized as slowly moving through a city. It is accepted in this case that the crime wave is not a physical reality in any sense, but a very useful statistical method of representing probabilities that events may happen in different parts of the city as time progresses. The essential point of such a concept is that no individual crime or action can be predicted, but nevertheless the statistical average of what may happen over the next month can often be predicted extremely accurately. It might therefore appear that the introduction of the wave concept is no more than an application of the mathematical probability pattern to the motion of electrons or quanta, both of which can now be considered as real particles, whose positions are just governed by certain probability rules. At first sight this does appear to be a way out of the dilemma, and a satisfactory concept of what is meant by the wave and particle approach. However, a close analysis of any of the diffraction or interference experiments which can be carried out with electrons or electromagnetic waves, will show that this idea can not in fact be maintained. In order to make this clear a rather careful analysis of the Young's double-slit interference experiment will be considered.

The double-slit interference experiment

One of the classic experiments that was performed to demonstrate the wave nature of light was the Young's double-slit experiment, illustrated schematically in Fig. 5.7. Rays of light from the source at S_1 fall onto the board (in the centre of the diagram) in which two small slits are cut at H_1 and H_2. The light transmitted by the slits then falls on the screen S and the light reaching a particular point P on this screen from the two slits is shown by the two rays on the diagram. It will be evident that the two slits in the centre board can now be considered as two separate sources of radiation, since they will both be receiving exactly the same light from the original source. The pattern of illumination that will be formed on the right-hand screen can therefore be deduced by considering the two rays as shown, which leave the slits in phase. Whether they will add, or cancel, when they combine at point P on the screen, will be determined by the length of the path difference between them. It is clear from the diagram that this path difference is given by H_2A and, provided $d \ll L$, the geometry of similar triangles will give

$$\frac{H_2A}{H_1H_2} = \frac{y}{L}. \tag{5.20}$$

For there to be constructive interference at P the distance H_2A must be equal to $n\lambda$ and hence the pattern of illumination on the screen will be a series of

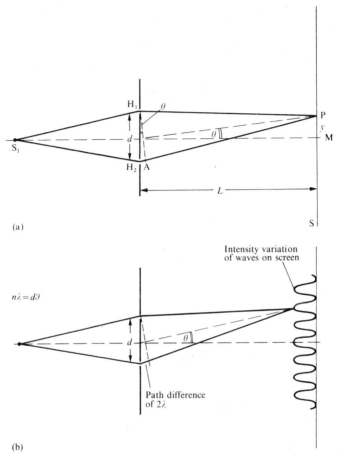

(a)

(b)

FIG. 5.7. Young's double-slit experiment. (a) Basic geometry. (b) Production of interference pattern—not to scale.

maxima and minima as shown in Fig. 5.7(b), with the positions of the maxima given by

$$n\lambda = d.\frac{y}{L} = d.\theta. \tag{5.21}$$

The production of this interference pattern with its consecutive maxima and minima across the screen, centred on the point opposite the mid-point of H_1H_2, is an experiment often conducted in school laboratories, and was one of the historically important experiments demonstrating the wave nature of light.

The particular importance of this experiment in the present context is that of recent years the sensitivities of detectors, both for individual quanta of radiation, and for individual electrons, have become so great that it is now possible to carry out this experiment with a source at S_1 which is so weak that individual quanta or electrons are only emitted one at a time, and at such an interval that only one of these is passing through the apparatus at any given time. The interesting question now arises whether one would still expect to see a single interference pattern due to *two* slits on the screen, or whether, instead, diffraction patterns corresponding to the two slits separately would be expected.

Thus if one of the slits is covered up, the pattern obtained under ordinary conditions of illumination would be a diffraction pattern due to a single slit, and this would be centred on the point opposite H_1 as shown in Fig. 5.8(a). If,

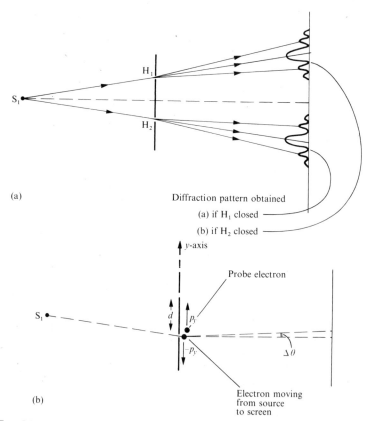

(a)

Diffraction pattern obtained

(a) if H_1 closed ——

(b) if H_2 closed ——

(b)

FIG. 5.8. Attempt to identify slit through which electron passes. (a) Diffraction patterns observed if either slit is closed. (b) Imagined use of probe electron.

on the other hand, the top slit was covered up and the bottom slit opened, then a second diffraction pattern is to be expected centred on the lower point indicated in Fig. 5.8(a). It is clear that the combination of these two patterns is quite different from that expected when both slits are open at once.

The question now arises, however, whether the single electron passing through the apparatus is to be considered as passing through both slits at the same time, or whether, under these conditions it must be considered as passing through either the top slit or the bottom slit, and hence taking part in the production of either the top diffraction pattern or the bottom diffraction pattern. Thus it can be very convincingly argued that a single electron passing through one of these slits cannot possibly know of the existence of the other slit, and therefore in such a case diffraction patterns, rather than the combined interference pattern, must surely be obtained. It is certainly clear that our normal concept of an individual particle rules out its passage through both slits simultaneously. Moreover, exactly the same argument can also be applied to the individual *quanta* that make up a beam of radiation. Again, since these can be detected individually under conditions in which only one passes through the apparatus at a time, it might be argued that under these conditions of illumination two diffraction patterns rather than a combined interference pattern are to be expected.

It is found experimentally however that, contrary to the arguments outlined above, the pattern of illumination on the screen always maintains the distribution corresponding to the combined interference pattern, even when only one electron or quantum is passing through the apparatus at a time. This result must imply that the wave nature to be associated with both the electron and the quantum is 'more real' than just a probability distribution, or statistical function.

The particular problem of the individual electron and which of the two slits it passes through, can be analysed in another way which again produces results of general interest. Thus we might argue that the true particle-nature of the electron could be demonstrated by determining which of the two slits it actually moves through during the interference experiment. Any measurement to determine this must be of a very delicate nature, however, so that it does not interfere with the actual experiment itself. We might imagine, therefore, that the best way to detect the presence of an electron going through the top slit would be to place a stationary electron at the far side, so that any passage of another electron through the slit would impart some momentum to the second electron as illustrated in Fig. 5.8(b). We could then observe this momentum acquisition, and hence be certain that the electron passing through the apparatus had indeed passed through the bottom slit. This kind of experimental arrangement is certainly possible in principle, but there are certain limitations which also apply to the observation due to the uncertainty principle, which it will be remembered states that it is impossible to measure both the position and momentum of an individual particle at the same time to a higher accuracy than that given by

$$\Delta x . \Delta p_x = \frac{h}{2\pi} \quad \text{and} \quad \Delta y . \Delta p_y = \frac{h}{2\pi}. \tag{5.22}$$

It is, moreover, imperative that we are certain about the position of the electron used for measurement to within a y-coordinate displacement of $\pm\frac{d}{2}$, since otherwise we will not be certain whether it is close to the top or the bottom hole when any momentum change occurs.

Let us now consider the amount of momentum change which it will experience if it is deflected by an electron passing through the slit during the interference experiment. Equal and opposite amounts of momenta will be interchanged between the two particles and we have already agreed that this change of momentum must not interfere too much with the experiment itself. In terms of destruction of the interference pattern it follows that the travelling electron must not be deflected by more than about $\Delta\theta/4$ where $\Delta\theta$ is the angle between successive maxima of the pattern and is given by eqn (5.21). We know also, however, that the wavelength of the electron is related to its momentum by the de Broglie expression, and hence we can combine these to say that the maximum change of momentum in a direction parallel to the screen, produced by the collision, for the electron travelling through the equipment is given by

$\Delta p_y = p . \dfrac{\Delta\theta}{4} = \dfrac{h}{\lambda} \times \dfrac{\lambda}{4d} = \dfrac{h}{4d}$. Combining the two conditions for the experiment, i.e. the restriction on the original position of the detecting electron, given in the last paragraph, and the restriction on the change of momentum in both electrons given by the above relation, one obtains the overall condition that

$\Delta p_y = p . \dfrac{\Delta\theta}{4} = \dfrac{h}{\lambda} \times \dfrac{\lambda}{4d} = \dfrac{h}{4d}$. Combining the two conditions for the experiment, categorically that for any electron, such as the electron we are using as the detecting probe, $\Delta y . \Delta p_y \geqslant h/2\pi$. It therefore follows from this analysis that it will be quite impossible, in principle, ever to determine the slit through which the electron passes, without destroying the interference pattern and the whole experiment in the process. This is another example of the fact that we cannot use any experimental means, or analysis, to prove conclusively that the electron is behaving like a 'real particle' and its wave-like properties can be ignored.

Waves and particles—the integrated picture

In our analysis of the different viewpoints that might be applicable to the wave–particle dualism, we have now eliminated the first three put forward on p. 77, and the only remaining one is the postulate that both the waves and particles are to some extent illusory and that neither of these are in fact perfect representations or analogies of either the quanta or the electrons. In the last section it was shown that we could not consider the electrons to be only particles, since in a very real sense they individually went through both of the slits in the experiment, but, when we come to consider what happens on the screen on the right of the apparatus, it is clear that they then possess very particle-like properties. Thus when we look at the interference pattern in detail, we realize that it is not all produced at any given instant, but it is formed by a continuous bombardment of the fluorescent screen by individual electrons or quanta, and the distribution of illumination on the screen comes from the statistical distribution of the individual particles as they hit the screen and emit visible radiation. In this part of the experiment, therefore, when we actually detect the interference pattern, either by a fluorescent screen or a bank of photocells, we are demonstrating very effectively the localized particle-like nature of both quanta and electrons. However it has become apparent that we must essentially be dealing with waves rather than particles when the quanta or electrons are traversing the slits in the middle of the apparatus.

Hence it is clear from the conditions of this experiment that both quanta and electrons have to be considered as both particles and waves in different parts of the equipment, and that neither of the two concepts on their own can completely account for the whole experiment. We are therefore forced to the conclusion that neither of these two descriptions can give a complete and accurate account of all the properties of either quanta or electrons, and hence both descriptions are to some extent illusory. It may appear at first sight that there must be a fundamental flaw in our conceptual framework if we cannot now give a description of the quanta of radiation, nor of electrons, in an unambiguous way. Further reflection, however, suggests that it is after all not surprising that neither the quantum of radiation, nor the electron, are exactly like anything we know, or can visualize, in the macroscopic world. Thus on the one hand we have been using the analogies and mental images of small billiard balls to describe our particles, and on the other hand mental images of waves on a vibrating string, or across the surface of a lake, to describe the properties of radiation. These mental images can only be imperfect analogies, however, and we are now forced to the conclusion that the real description of either an electron or a quantum of energy cannot be made in terms of a perfect analogy with any macroscopic phenomenon. In fact the only perfectly true and correct representation of either will be by a mathematical equation, which can be solved to give us accurate predictions for various properties that can be measured, i.e. the position or momentum of the electron or quantum, but cannot give us a more tangible mental image, since no object in the macroscopic world will possess exactly the same properties.

We find, therefore, that the dilemma with which we are faced, concerning the dual nature of radiation and matter, is to be solved by recognizing that the fault lies in our own mental images and not in the behavior of the entities themselves. Mental images such as billiard balls or ripples across the surface of a lake are extremely helpful when trying to visualize concepts as they are initially met, but as often happens in the development of physics, advance takes place as the original mental images have to be discarded and replaced by a more abstract concept. Thus it is with both the study of radiation and matter, and the rapid development of the theory of wave mechanics which followed de Broglie's original suggestions showed how advance could be made in this way.

The wave equation

Although this text is primarily concerned with radiation, it has already been seen that there is very close duality between the properties of radiation and of matter, and it would be inappropriate to leave this chapter without a brief introduction to the wave equation as it has been developed to represent the properties of electrons, and other particles.

One might say, without generalizing too much, that the whole idea of wave mechanics and the new approach to theoretical physics is based on two fundamental concepts, i.e. (i) that waves can be associated with moving particles, according to the de Broglie relation, and (ii) that only standing wave patterns can store energy in a system, and only travelling waves transmit energy from one system to another. The application of these two basic concepts to the hydrogen atom gives immediate justification for Bohr's postulates of stationary orbits. Thus instead of arbitrarily defining the allowed orbits as those which possess angular momenta $= n \times h/2\pi$ we can now define the allowed electron orbits as those around which a stationary wave pattern can be established, and hence orbits which can store energy, as illustrated diagrammatically in Fig. 5.9. The calculation of the allowed orbits now

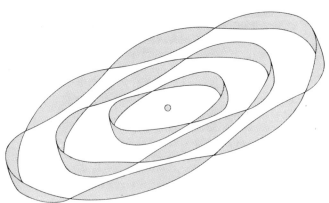

FIG. 5.9. Standing waves in allowed electronic orbits.

resolves itself into a calculation of the wavelengths associated with the electrons in the orbits concerned, and the stationary orbits will then be those in which the circumference is equal to $n\lambda$. The fact that these allowed orbits are those originally predicted by Bohr follows from the relation that $\lambda = h/mv$ and also equals $2\pi r/n$. Hence $h/mv = 2\pi r/n$ and $mvr = n(h/2\pi)$ which is Bohr's original postulate. The results of Bohr's theory still hold, but the approach of wave mechanics now gives the underlying reason why certain orbits are allowed and others are not. The general concept of standing waves thus replaces the arbitrary postulates put forward by Bohr.

When a full wave-mechanical treatment of the hydrogen atom is carried through, it is found that other quantum numbers also come directly from the mathematical solutions, and can be equated to the number of times an expression can be integrated, or the number of surfaces passing through a point, and which can only have any meaning if they are integers. The very existence of quantum numbers can then be said to be associated with the basic properties of the spatial representation of the wave patterns themselves, and do not appear as arbitrary integers inserted to make theory agree with experiment.

Although it is fairly easy to see how the concept of stationary wave patterns can be applied to the orbits of the hydrogen atom, it is also clear that a more general and sophisticated theory must be developed to deal with the general three-dimensional case. It was the development of such a theory by Schrödinger that introduced the subject of wave mechanics, which, together with the other formulation of quantum mechanics, revolutionized the whole field of theoretical physics. A very brief analysis of how a more general wave equation can be deduced will now be given.

The general way in which a wave may be treated mathematically can probably be best approached by considering the simple case of a wave on a string. A short length of such a string is shown in Fig. 5.10 and the particular element δL is shown making projections δx on the x-axis, δy along the y-axis, which measures the amplitude of the wave, and angles to the x-axis of θ and $(\theta + \delta\theta)$ at its two ends.

The equation of motion of this element of string in the y-direction may now be written as

$$T \sin (\theta + \delta\theta) - T \sin \theta = \rho.\delta x.\frac{\partial^2 y}{\partial t^2} \tag{5.23}$$

where T is the tension in the string and ρ is the mass per unit length. If θ is small, $\sin \theta \approx \theta \approx \dfrac{\delta y}{\delta x}$ and hence

$$(\theta + \delta\theta) \approx \frac{\delta y}{\delta x} + \left(\frac{\partial \theta}{\partial x}\right) \delta x = \frac{\delta y}{\delta x} + \frac{\partial^2 y}{\partial x^2}.\delta x.$$

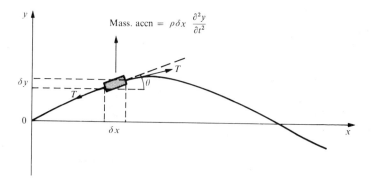

Fɪɢ. 5.10. Wave on a string. Analysis of motion parallel to the y-axis.

The equation of motion then becomes

$$T.\frac{\partial^2 y}{\partial x^2}.\delta x = \rho.\frac{\partial^2 y}{\partial t^2}.\delta x$$

$$\frac{\partial^2 y}{\partial x^2} = \frac{\rho}{T}.\frac{\partial^2 y}{\partial t^2}. \qquad (5.24)$$

Such a differential equation represents the general mathematical form of a wave travelling in one dimension along the x-axis, with a velocity given by the square root of the inverse of the coefficient multiplying $\partial^2 y/\partial t^2$, i.e. $v = (T/\rho)^{\frac{1}{2}}$ in this case.

If the more general case of a wave moving in three dimensions is considered the equation has the same form but becomes generalized to

$$\frac{\partial^2 \psi}{\partial x^2} + \frac{\partial^2 \psi}{\partial y^2} + \frac{\partial^2 \psi}{\partial z^2} = \frac{1}{v^2}.\frac{\partial^2 \psi}{\partial t^2} \qquad (5.25)$$

where ψ is the amplitude of the wave.

It has been seen that only stationary wave patterns will store energy, and hence represent energy levels of the electrons or atoms in question. The equation for a simple stationary sine wave in one dimension may be written

$$\psi_{(x,t)} = A \sin\frac{2\pi x}{\lambda}.\sin 2\pi vt \qquad (5.26)$$

and the more general equation is

$$\psi_{(x,t)} = \phi(x).\sin 2\pi vt \qquad (5.27)$$

where ϕ is a time-independent amplitude function.

It follows that for such a wave

$$\frac{\partial^2 \psi}{\partial t^2} = -4\pi^2 v^2 . \sin 2\pi vt . \phi(x) \tag{5.28}$$

$$\frac{\partial^2 \psi}{\partial x^2} = \sin 2\pi vt . \frac{\partial^2 \phi(x)}{\partial x^2} . \tag{5.29}$$

If these two expressions are now substituted into the one-dimensional case of eqn (5.25) we obtain

$$\sin 2\pi vt \frac{\partial^2 \phi(x)}{\partial x^2} = -\frac{1}{v^2} . 4\pi^2 v^2 . \sin 2\pi vt . \phi(x)$$

$$\therefore \quad \frac{\partial^2 \phi(x)}{\partial x^2} + \frac{4\pi^2 v^2}{v^2} . \phi(x) = 0. \tag{5.30}$$

Since $v = \lambda v$ the equation may be written

$$\frac{\partial^2 \phi(x)}{\partial x^2} + \frac{4\pi^2}{\lambda^2} . \phi(x) = 0 \tag{5.31}$$

which is a general equation giving the solutions for the time-independent amplitude of any stationary wave pattern, and can also be generalized to the three-dimensional case, as before.

So far in this analysis no consideration of matter waves, as such, has been introduced, but the general equation (eqn 5.31) can now be applied to electron waves by using the De Broglie relation to substitute for λ and replace it by $h/(2mE)^{\frac{1}{2}}$, if the electron energy is entirely kinetic.

The wave equation for stationary electron waves now becomes

$$\frac{\partial^2 \phi(x)}{\partial x^2} + 4\pi^2 \left(\frac{2mE}{h^2} \right) . \phi(x) = 0 \tag{5.32}$$

and if the electron possesses potential energy V_x as well as kinetic energy, then the wave equation will become

$$\frac{\partial^2 \phi(x)}{\partial x^2} + \frac{8\pi^2 m}{h^2} (E - V_x) . \phi(x) = 0. \tag{5.33}$$

This is, in fact, the one-dimensional form of the famous Schrödinger Wave Equation, and in its more general form, it can be applied to any physical system to determine the allowed stationary wave patterns, and hence allowed energy-storing states.

The actual solution of the equation in any given system involves a substitution of the suitable expression for V_x and then the application of appropriate boundary conditions. Details of the way in which this wave equation is in fact evaluated in specific cases are beyond the scope of this book, but it is of considerable interest to see how its original formulation arose out of the search for a deeper understanding of the nature of matter and radiation.

PROBLEMS

5.1. A high energy γ-ray photon collides with a stationary electron and is deflected through an angle of $30°$ in the process. Calculate the resultant change in its wavelength.

5.2. Calculate the absolute change and the fractional change in wavelength for (i) X-rays of 10^{-1} nm wavelength, and (ii) visible radiation of 500 nm wavelength, when they are scattered through $90°$ by collision with an electron.

5.3. Calculate the wavelength of the wave associated with (i) a satellite weighing 100 kg travelling at 40 000 km s^{-1} (ii) a photon of electromagnetic radiation of 1 MeV energy (iii) a proton with 1 MeV kinetic energy.

5.4. In experiments on electron diffraction by a nickel crystal it was found that the first diffraction maximum occurred at an angle of reflection of $50°$. If the spacing between the nickel atoms was 0·215 nm determine the velocity with which the electrons were moving and the voltage through which they had been accelerated.

5.5. Calculate the velocity which a beam of neutrons must possess if the same diffraction maximum is to be obtained for them as for the electrons in Problem 5.4. (Neutron mass $= 1·67 \times 10^{-27}$ kg.)

5.6. Neutrons in a beam emerging from a nuclear reactor have kinetic energies varying from zero to a few electron volts. They are incident on a crystal face which has a spacing of 0·28 nm between its atomic layers. Calculate the angle between the incident beam and the crystal face if the reflected neutrons are to have an energy of 0·25 eV.

5.7. If the velocity of (i) an electron and (ii) a droplet of water of radius 10^{-2} mm are known to an accuracy of 10^{-3} m s^{-1}, calculate the maximum accuracy with which their position coordinates can be known.

5.8. Given that the radius of a typical nucleus is 5×10^{-15} m, and that the average binding energy for nucleons within the nucleus is 8 MeV, show from the uncertainty principles that it is not possible for an electron to exist within the nucleus.

5.9. If all other sources of broadening are removed from a spectral line the 'natural width' associated with the limited life-time of its excited state still remains. Calculate the ratio of this width, in frequency units, to the frequency of the spectral line itself for (i) a line in the visible region of 6 000 Å wavelength and excited state lifetime of 10^{-8} sec, (ii) a γ-ray emission line of 1 Å wavelength and excited-state lifetime of 10^{-12} seconds.

5.10. For what wavelength will an electron and photon have the same kinetic energy and wavelength? (*Hint:* Use relativistic mechanics.)

6. The interaction of radiation with matter

Coherent and incoherent radiation

PREVIOUS chapters have been concerned with the general properties of radiation. Although some consideration has been given to the different ways in which radiation can be produced, no systematic study of the ways in which radiation interacts with matter has yet been attempted. Such interactions are discussed in this chapter beginning with the general processes of absorption and emission as they occur between any pair of energy levels—molecular, atomic, or nuclear.

It might appear from Chapter 4 that the only requirement for the production of visible radiation is some means of exciting atomic electrons into a higher state, so that they can then revert to the ground state and emit the radiation in the process. There is one important concept, however, which has not yet been considered and that is the phase relationship which may exist between successive quanta, as they are emitted from such an atomic source. Thus, although they will all have the same frequency, if originating from the same pair of energy levels, there may be no correlation between the phases of successive wave-trains. The concept of correlated phase can probably be best visualized in terms of radio-waves transmitted from a dipole aerial, as already illustrated in Fig. 4.3. The pulses of current producing these waves are driven by a master oscillator, and the wave-train produced will be of the form shown in Fig. 6.1(a). Moreover, if the amplifying circuit between the master oscillator and the aerial is momentarily disconnected, and then reconnected, the waves will continue with exactly the same relation to those initially propagated, as in Fig. 6.1(b), and phase coherence is maintained despite the intermission. In contrast, the wave-trains emitted from successive excitations of an atom, or by a group of identical atoms, will normally have no such phase coherence, as shown in Fig. 6.1(c).

The great importance of this phase coherence in radio-signals arises from the fact that it is then possible to modulate such a coherent carrier wave with lower-frequency signals, and thus pass a whole range of information on the single carrier wave. The amount of information carried will depend on the bandwidth, or the frequency coverage, of the modulation that is being employed, but a large number of simultaneous telephone conversations can readily be impressed on a single radio-frequency carrier wave. This will be quite impossible, however, if the carrier wave consists of bursts of incoherent wave-trains, which have phase patterns that are completely uncorrelated.

Radio-waves, and microwaves at slightly higher frequencies, are used

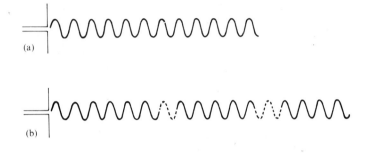

(a)

(b)

(c)

FIG. 6.1. Emission of coherent and incoherent wave-trains from aerial. (a) Continuous coherent wave-train. (b) Intermittent but coherent wave-train. (c) Incoherent wave-trains.

extensively for the transmission of information because the frequency and phase of such waves can be readily controlled by the electronic devices which produce the radiation, and hence they can be readily modulated. It is, however, only in recent years that it has been possible to produce coherent visible radiation and hence open up the whole of this region for the transmission of complex information.

It will be appreciated that there is no 'master oscillator' in a collection of atoms emitting visible light from an ordinary source and hence random and incoherent wave-trains are to be expected. In order to appreciate how it is possible to produce coherent visible light from an atomic source the three basic processes whereby radiation can interact with atomic energy levels must be considered.

These are illustrated in Fig. 6.2. In Fig. 6.2(a) the basic process of absorption is illustrated. The incoming quantum of radiation is absorbed by the atom and the energy is used to excite the atom, or its electron, to a higher energy level as shown. Fig. 6.2(b) shows the inverse of this process, i.e. spontaneous emission, where the atom or electron in the higher energy level reverts to the ground state and emits a quantum of energy in the process. This spontaneous emission will take place in the complete absence of any initiating factor and the normal kind of lifetime between absorption and spontaneous emission for an atomic electron will be about 10^{-9} second. It is clear that in this case there is nothing with which the phase of the emitted wave can be compared and hence successive emissions from this atom, or others, will be completely uncorrelated in phase. Incoherent radiation is thus produced when spontaneous emission takes place.

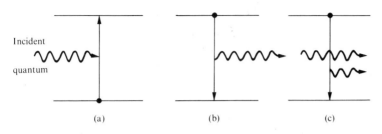

FIG. 6.2. The three basic processes whereby radiation interacts with matter. (a) Absorption. (b) Spontaneous emission. (c) Stimulated emission.

Fig. 6.2(c), however, shows another type of emission which can occur, termed stimulated emission, which takes place when the atom or electron is already in the upper state, but is triggered off to revert to the ground state by an incoming quantum of energy of the same frequency. This incoming quantum is not itself absorbed because the atom is already in the higher energy level, but it serves as an initiating trigger to release the stored energy and produces a second quantum of the same frequency, earlier than expected by spontaneous emission. Moreover the emitted quantum is now in step with the initiating quantum and there is complete phase coherence between the two wave-trains as shown in the figure. It is clear that such an interaction provides the basis for coherent radiation, and all that is required for a practical source of coherent radiation is to devise a system in which the incoming quantum is more likely to produce stimulated emission than to produce absorption.

A whole range of new devices have come into existence over the last few years based on this principle of stimulated emission. The *laser* (*l*ight *a*mplification by *s*timulated *e*mission of *r*adiation) is an example in the visible region. To produce the required higher probability for stimulated emission, rather than absorption, it is necessary to invert the usual distribution of atoms between the two energy levels. Thus any system in thermal equilibrium with its surroundings will always have a larger number of atoms in the lower energy state. Moreover, fairly early in the development of radiation theory Einstein showed that the coefficients of absorption and stimulated emission must be equal, and hence their respective probabilities of actually occurring will be determined entirely by the number of atoms in the lower and upper state, as indicated in Fig. 6.3.

The design and construction of lasers thus required the development of processes whereby atoms can be continuously fed into the upper energy state at a rate faster than they come down during the emission process. A large variety of different types of mechanism have now been invented for this purpose, but most of these are based upon some kind of three-level pumping system as illustrated in Fig. 6.4. In this system the stimulated emission is

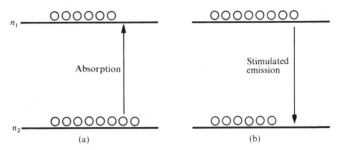

FIG. 6.3. Energy-level population inversion. In (a) normal thermal equilibrium gives $n_1 < n_2$ and hence absorption dominates. In (b) the population is inverted, $n_1 > n_2$ and stimulated emission dominates.

produced between levels B and C, and in order to produce dominant emission rather than absorption, for this transition, it is necessary to invert the usual energy-level population given by $n_B/n_C = \exp(E_{BC}/kT)$ so that n_C becomes greater than n_B. This may be effected if a large amount of energy is fed into the system at the higher frequency ν_{AC} so that the numbers in levels A and C are nearly equalized and there is thus a continual replacement of those used in the stimulated emission process. The first successful laser systems employed very high energy photoflashes to drive the chromium atoms in a piece of ruby from the ground state to the higher level, thus inverting the population distribution of the intermediate states, when the laser emits its characteristic red ruby light as a series of coherent waves.

There is no space for the details of the many laser systems that have been developed since that time, but the ready availability of coherent light in the visible region has a large number of very interesting applications. These include those in communication, where the modulation of the coherent waves becomes a possibility, and also those in such fields as surgery, where the very high energy-densities which can be fed down a coherent-wave beam can be

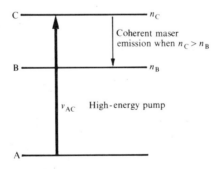

FIG. 6.4. The three-level maser.

used for incision purposes. On the more academic side, it should be noted that the availability of coherent sources which can produce plane parallel waves over a relatively large wave-front, now makes it very much easier to demonstrate a large range of interference effects. For instance, the Young's double-slit experiment discussed in some detail in the last chapter, no longer requires a point source to be equidistant from two slits in a screen. Instead the two slits can simply be placed in front of the plane waves emitted from a flat laser surface, since all the waves along this wave-front will be coherent.

Quantum detectors

In the last section the emission of radiation from energy-level systems was considered in some detail, but another development of recent years has been the detection of very small quantities of incoming radiation via its interaction with quantized energy levels. Specific excitation in these levels often alters the bulk properties of the material in a way that can be readily measured. Such detecting devices will normally only operate efficiently for a given wavelength or range of wavelengths associated with the particular excitation which is induced. Since the excitation normally takes the form of an electron raised to a higher energy level, such detectors can be grouped together under the general heading of electronic quantum detectors.

One very straightforward example of such quantum detectors may be found in the infrared region, where the incoming radiation can be used to excite electrons from impurity levels in a semiconductor into the conduction levels, and hence produce an appreciable increase in the conductivity of the specimen. The onset of this enhanced conductivity can then be readily measured and used to indicate the presence of the incoming radiation. Examples of such infrared quantum detectors are lead sulphide which has an energy separation corresponding to wavenumbers around $3\,000\ \mathrm{cm}^{-1}$ and indium antimonide which will detect wavelengths very efficiently near $1\,800\ \mathrm{cm}^{-1}$.

As the frequency of incident radiation rises so will the energy of the excited electron in the absorbing material. It has already been seen in earlier chapters, when discussing the photoelectric effect, that for frequencies above the cut-off corresponding to the work function of the material, the electrons can be excited sufficiently to be ejected from the material as photoelectrons. In fact one of the practical methods of detecting incident ultraviolet radiation is via the photo-electric effect. This can be made very much more sensitive by the initiation of a chain reaction, in which the first ejected photoelectron is accelerated towards a second active metal surface where its impact releases several secondary electrons, which are in turn accelerated to a third surface where the secondary electrons produce several tertiary electrons. This whole process is then repeated some ten or more times within the one photomultiplier tube, each stage having about 100 volts accelerating potential across it. As a result the single photo-electron originally ejected may produce more than a million at the end of the photomultiplier and these then constitute a current of sufficiently large magnitude to activate macroscopic recording devices.

X-rays and their interaction with matter

The way in which X-rays and γ-rays can be produced by transitions between well spaced electronic levels on the one hand, and from internal nuclear levels on the other, has been briefly summarized in Chapter 1. It was also pointed out that a high percentage of the X-rays produced from a normal X-ray tube were continuous, or 'bremsstrahlung' radiation, formed when the high-velocity electrons were rapidly decelerated. Examples of both types of radiation are shown in Fig. 6.5, where the intensity output from an X-ray tube is plotted

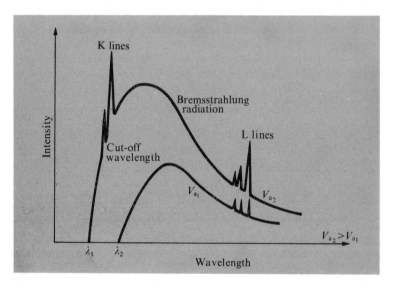

Fig. 6.5. Variation of intensity of emitted X-rays with wavelength for two different anode voltages.

against wavelength for two different voltages at the anode. For the lower voltage the intensity distribution is seen to follow a smooth curve, and all the emitted radiation is of the 'braking' or 'bremsstrahlung' type.

For the higher anode voltage, well-defined peaks occur in the intensity distribution, however, corresponding to precise spectral lines. These will be obtained when the incident electrons from the cathode have enough energy to displace one of the inner K- or L-shell electrons of the atoms in the metal anode. An outer electron can then fall in to fill the vacancy, emitting an X-ray of precise energy and frequency as it does so. The observed frequencies, or wavelengths, can then be correlated with the different energy levels of the atom, as indicated in the figure.

In the same way that spectral lines are observed in the *emission* spectra of X-rays, so their absorption spectra show characteristic 'edges' or sudden changes, when the incident wavelength is equal to that of the inner K- or L-electron-shell transitions.

If the line shapes of the X-ray emission spectra are observed more closely, however, structure can sometimes be seen. This arises from the fact that the energy levels are not single precise energies but are smeared out into a 'band' by the solid state interactions of the metal anode. This spread of energy will be reflected in the line shape of the X-ray emission itself, and an example of such a line is shown in Fig. 6.6.

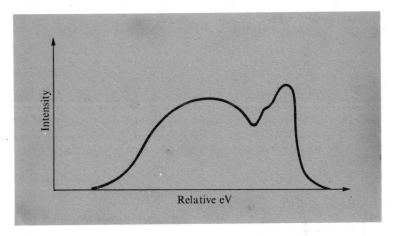

FIG. 6.6. Detailed line shape of X-ray emission line from aluminium metal. Total line width is of the order of 20 electronvolts.

This particular pattern was obtained from aluminium and it is clearly formed from two main lines which overlap. These are, in fact, the 3s and 3p bands, the spread and overlap of which can be seen and measured.

Detailed theories on the spread and structure of such energy bands within the solid have developed very considerably over recent years, and can be correlated with a large number of the electronic properties of both metals and semiconductors. There are relatively few direct methods whereby the spread and structure of the bands can be determined experimentally, however, and X-ray emission spectroscopy can thus be used as a powerful probe in solid-state physics, as well as in the study of the deeper atomic levels themselves.

The simplest explanation of the background bremsstrahlung radiation is in terms of a continuously decelerated electric charge, which will, on Maxwell's theory, produce electromagnetic radiation. The rapid deceleration at the anode of the X-ray tube will produce the high frequency X-rays observed. However such a theory cannot be complete because one of the most striking features of both curves in Fig. 6.5 is that they have a very definite cut-off frequency, and this is given by the quantitative relation

$$h\nu_{\text{cut-off}} = eV_a$$

where V_a is the accelerating voltage on the anode. Such a relation immediately implies a quantization of the emitted radiation, and the maximum frequency of emission will then be obtained when the maximum energy which an electron can acquire during its flight across the tube (eV_a) is given to an individual quantum. It is in fact possible to produce a full quantum-mechanical theory of the bremsstrahlung radiation, but the details of this are beyond the scope of this book.

γ-Ray emission—the Mossbauer effect

It has already been seen that γ-rays can be produced in the same way as X-rays—either by the rapid deceleration of very fast electrons, or from a transition between two energy levels. In the case of γ-rays the energy levels will be associated with the forces within the nucleus, of both a nuclear and electrostatic type, instead of simply the electrostatic forces which bind the electrons to the atom.

In the case of the γ-ray spectral lines obtained from decaying nuclei it is often found that the emission of the γ-ray follows the emission of an α-particle, when one nucleus decays to a set of alternative excited states of the second. An example of this is shown in Fig. 6.7, where the energy level of the parent $^{212}_{83}\text{Bi}$ is shown together with the different energy levels of the daughter radioactive product, $^{208}_{81}\text{Tl}$. It will be seen from this diagram that it is possible for the parent $^{212}_{83}\text{Bi}$ to decay directly to the ground state of the daughter nucleus, by the direct emission of an α-particle, indicated as α_0, which, together with the nuclear recoil (0·11 MeV) removes the total energy difference between the two states. However, it is also possible for the parent nucleus to emit an α-particle and decay to one of the intermediate excited states of the daughter $^{208}_{81}\text{Tl}$, and this excited state will then in turn emit a γ-ray and drop down to the ground state. The validity of this picture is established by the fact that the difference in energy between the emitted α-particles exactly corresponds to the difference in energies of the excited states of the daughter nucleus as deduced from the emitted γ-ray spectra. High-energy γ-ray photons emitted from radioactive nuclei in this way normally have a spread of energy associated with them, since the momentum which they acquire on emission must be balanced by an

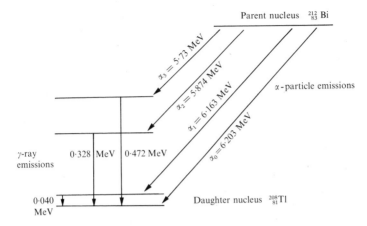

FIG. 6.7. Decay scheme for $^{212}_{83}$Bi to $^{208}_{81}$Tl. γ-Ray emissions from the excited states of $^{208}_{83}$Tl are seen to match the difference in α-particle energies.

equal and opposite amount given to the recoiling nucleus, and some of the energy of the nuclear transition will therefore be lost to the nucleus.

Mossbauer discovered in 1958, however, that the energy of emission of some γ-rays emitted from solid specimens was extremely precise and had apparently lost no energy to the recoiling nucleus. This can only be explained if it is assumed that the whole of the crystal lattice takes part in the recoil process. Thus if the emitted γ-ray has a frequency v_0, its momentum, and hence the momentum of the recoiling nucleus or lattice, will be hv_0/c. The kinetic energy of the recoiling nucleus, or lattice, will be given by

$$\tfrac{1}{2}mv^2 = (\text{momentum})^2/2m = (hv_0)^2/2m.$$

It is clear that the energy taken up by the recoiling body, and therefore lost by the γ-ray photon, is inversely proportional to the mass of the body. Thus although the loss of energy may be significant for a single nuclear mass, it will be completely negligible for the crystal as a whole with a mass some 10^{20} times greater.

The energies of γ-ray photons from such 'recoilless' emissions are therefore very precise, and limited only by the uncertainty principle, and hence the lifetime of the excited state. Thus for a lifetime of 10^{-7} s the energy spread of the emission line as measured at half-height will be given by $\Delta E = h/2\pi\,\Delta\tau$; or, in frequency units, $\Delta v = (2\pi\,.\Delta\tau)^{-1} = 1\cdot6$ MHz.

Since the γ-ray photon itself will have a frequency of about 3×10^{12} MHz, it follows that the possible precision and resolution in measurements employing such transitions may be as high as 1 part in 10^{12}. For shorter lifetimes they can be significantly higher still.

In order to take any spectroscopic measurements with such a mono-chromatic source it will be necessary to change the frequency systematically, however, so that a range of wavelengths is available, to sweep through and plot out the absorption curve of the specimen to be studied. Very fortunately this range can be provided by the application of the Doppler effect which is observed for a source in motion. For a velocity v, relative to the observer, the frequency measured by the observer is changed by a factor $\Delta v = v.v/c$.

Hence relative velocities of the order of $(\Delta v/v)c$ are required, and thus for a frequency range ten times the width of the emission line, a velocity of

$$(10/10^{12}) \times 3 \times 10^8 = 3 \times 10^{-3} \text{ m s}^{-1}$$

is needed. Such a velocity of a few mm per second is obviously relatively easy to produce in practice and may be obtained, for instance, by mounting the source on a microphone coil. The experimental requirements for Mossbauer spectroscopy are therefore very simple and straightforward, i.e. an emitting source, such as a crystal containing ^{57}Fe, mounted on a platform that can be set in motion at various speeds. The absorption spectrum of ^{57}Fe nuclei located in a different type of crystal lattice can then be studied by plotting the number of γ-rays transmitted through the specimen against the velocity of the emitting source, and thus, effectively, against γ-ray wavelength.

The various interactions which are present within the crystal lattice, such as the effect of the internal crystalline field on the nuclear quadrupole moment, and hence on the energy of the emitted γ-ray, can then be studied in extreme detail, and hence another very precise probe is available for solid-state investigations. The main limitation of Mossbauer spectroscopy at the moment is set by the limited number of nuclei which produce suitable γ-ray emissions. Those used to date include ^{57}Fe, ^{61}Ni, ^{67}Zn, ^{119}Sn, ^{129}I and ^{197}Au.

Scattering and pair-production

Quite apart from their use in the Mossbauer effect, γ-rays emitted from nuclei, whether naturally or artificially radioactive, can be used to map out the energy-level system of the nucleus in much the same way that visible and u.v. spectra enabled the electronic energy systems of atoms to be determined. It is, however, possible for both γ-rays and X-rays to interact with matter in other ways, and these will now be briefly considered.

The interactions can be grouped under three major headings: (i) photo-electric effect, (ii) Compton scattering, and (iii) pair-production. The first two of these have already been considered in some detail. Although the dis-cussion of the photoelectric effect in Chapter 3 was primarily concerned with incident visible or u.v. quanta, it is clear that higher-energy quanta will also cause ejection of photoelectrons from the material. For energies of the incident quanta up to 1 MeV, the photoelectric effect will be the most probable mechanism whereby the incoming X-ray or γ-ray loses energy, especially for atoms of higher atomic number. In this process all of the energy of the quantum is given to the single electron, which is then ejected with a kinetic energy equal to that of the incident quantum less the ionization energy or work-function energy of the atom or material concerned.

In the case of Compton scattering, which was considered in some detail in Chapter 5, only part of the energy of the incident photon is absorbed, and the rest is carried away by the scattered photon with its longer wavelength and lower frequency, the balance of energy being taken away by the recoiling electron. This scattering process takes place over a wide range of incident energies, but its probability takes over from the photoelectric effect at an incident photon energy of about 2 MeV as is indicated in Fig. 6.8. At higher energies than this the probability for both the photoelectric effect and the Compton scattering begins to fall quite noticeably, and quite another type of interaction, known as pair-production, then takes over.

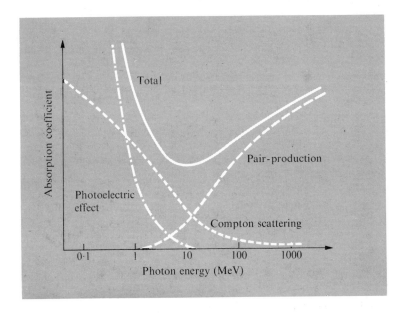

FIG. 6.8. Comparison of absorption coefficients due to different interactions of high-energy radiation with matter—for heavy atoms such as lead.

The fact that matter can be converted into energy on the basis of Einstein's equation $E = mc^2$, is very well known, and the basis of nuclear power. It is also possible, however, for this interaction to take place in the reverse direction, and for energy in the form of electromagnetic radiation to be converted directly into matter, but in this case it is clear that a very large amount of energy will be required to produce a small quantity of matter. If such an interaction is to take place, however, two other conservation laws must also be fulfilled, i.e. conservation of electric charge and conservation of linear momentum. Thus it is impossible to create just one single electron from a γ-ray, since electric charge would not be conserved before and after the event. The production of any charged particle will therefore require a simultaneous production of its opposite partner for charge to be conserved. It follows from this that the minimum γ-ray energy that will be able to be converted into matter is that equivalent to twice the rest mass of the electron and given by

$$h\nu = 2m_0c^2, \tag{6.1}$$

which on substitution of the appropriate values gives a minimum energy of 1·022 MeV. It can be seen from Fig. 6.8 that the production of electron pairs by absorption of γ-rays does not start taking place until the incident energy has risen above 1 MeV, but that as the energy rises, so the probability of pair-production quickly increases.

It is interesting to see how the two other conservation conditions can be met simultaneously, i.e. the conservation of energy and the conservation of momentum, when a single γ-ray photon is converted into an electron–positron pair. This interaction is represented schematically in Fig. 6.9, and can be analysed as follows.

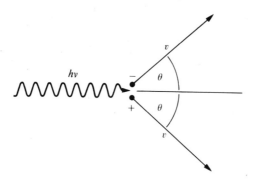

FIG. 6.9. Principle of pair-production, near a nucleus.

The application of the principle of conservation of energy gives

where

$$h\nu = 2mc^2 \tag{6.2}$$

$$m = m_0 \Big/ \left(1 - \frac{v^2}{c^2}\right)^{\frac{1}{2}}; \tag{6.3}$$

while the application of the principle of conservation of linear momentum along the original direction of the γ-ray photon gives

$$\frac{h\nu}{c} = 2mv \cos \theta. \tag{6.4}$$

Comparison of eqn (6.2) and (6.4) shows that $c = v \cos \theta$ and hence $v > c$. This condition is quite impossible to fulfill, however, because the electron cannot travel faster than light, as evidenced by eqn (6.3).

It therefore follows that it is impossible for a γ-ray to change spontaneously into matter when moving through empty space, however great its energy might be. For pair-production to take place there must be some third body present, such as a nucleus, to take part in the energy–momentum conservation. A similar analysis of the photoelectric effect will show that there must be a sharing of energy and momentum with a third body in this case also, but this is not so surprising since here the electron is initially regarded as bound to an atom, or within a solid lattice.

Microwave spectroscopy and magnetic resonance

Spectroscopy has advanced fairly rapidly at both ends of the electro-magnetic spectrum in recent years. Thus at the same time as precise information was being obtained on nuclear energy levels from γ-ray emission spectra, so very accurate measurements on spectral lines in the microwave and radio-regions of the spectra were giving information on molecular and solid-state forces and interactions.

As well as the straightforward absorption spectra that are obtained when microwaves are passed through gaseous samples, two other techniques which are very good examples of quantum resonance methods have been developed, known as electron and nuclear resonance, respectively.

In both electron resonance, carried out at microwave frequencies, and in nuclear resonance carried out at radio-frequencies, a magnetic field is applied externally and this then interacts with magnetic moments within the specimen—with the moment of the electron spin in the first case, and with that of the nucleus in the second.

The theories of these two effects can therefore be studied side by side as is illustrated in Fig. 6.10 for the case of electrons and protons. In the absence of any applied field the electrons in the one case, and the protons in the other, can point in any direction and will all have the same energy. When a magnetic field is applied, however, the magnetic moments of the particles will align themselves either parallel or anti-parallel to the direction of the field. They will thus be divided into two groups, and these groups will have different energies since the energy of interaction of a magnetic moment in a field, B, is given by μB, μ being the resolved component of the moment in the direction of the field.

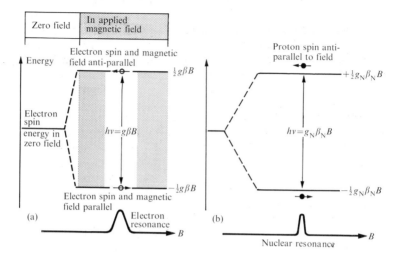

FIG. 6.10. Basic principles of electron and nuclear magnetic resonance. (a) Electron Resonance $v = 2\cdot8 \times 10^{10}.B$ Hz. (b) Nuclear Resonance $v = 4\cdot26 \times 10^7.B$ Hz.

The magnetic moment of an electron is given by $\frac{1}{2}g\beta$ where β is the Bohr magneton, equal to $eh/4\pi m$ and g has a value of 2·0 for a completely free electron. The energies of the two groups of electrons will therefore be $\pm\frac{1}{2}g\beta.B$ respectively, with a separation of $g\beta B$ as shown in the figure.

The magnetic moment of a proton is given by $\frac{1}{2}g_N\beta_N$ where β_N is the nuclear magneton, equal to $eh/4\pi M$ and hence about 1 000 times smaller than the Bohr magneton. An energy separation of $g_N\beta_N B$ between the two groups of protons is therefore produced, which, for the same field B, will be about 1 000 times smaller than that for the electrons.

In both techniques a resonant absorption is produced by applying radiation of frequency v, such that hv is equal to the energy gap, as indicated in the figure. In the case of electron resonance the condition therefore becomes

$$hv = g\beta B, \tag{6.5}$$

or

$$v = 2\cdot8 \times 10^{10}.B \text{ Hz}, \tag{6.6}$$

for a free electron, with spin-only magnetism, and with B measured in tesla (10^4 gauss). For a field of 1 tesla, which is about the maximum that can be readily provided in the laboratory without superconducting magnets, the required resonant frequency will be 28 000 MHz—i.e. a wavelength of about 1 cm, in the middle of the microwave region.

When such resonance radiation is applied the electrons will be excited from the ground state to the higher level, absorbing the microwave radiation in the process. The characteristics of the electrons bound within the solid can thus be determined by studying the microwave absorption line so produced. Its resonance position determines its g-value and hence gives information on the orbital contribution to its magnetism and thus the type of binding present in the specimen; its linewidth is determined by the various spin–spin and spin–lattice interactions within the solid; while any hyperfine structure on the line will give information on the properties of the nucleus around which it is moving.

Electron resonance studies have in fact been made on a large number of different types of solid to obtain such information, including metals, semiconductors, transition group compounds, irradiated crystals, and polymers, as well as a wide range of chemical and biochemical compounds.

In a similar way the protons can be excited from their ground state to the higher level if a resonant radio-frequency v is employed where

$$hv = g_N\beta_N B \tag{6.7}$$

or

$$v = 4{\cdot}258 \times 10^7 . B \text{ Hz} \tag{6.8}$$

for a proton. In this case a field of 1 tesla will require a resonant frequency of 42·6 MHz—i.e. in the radio-frequency region, and the techniques employed will involve inductance coils and capacitors instead of the microwave cavities used in electron resonance.

In its initial studies nuclear resonance was employed to measure unknown nuclear spins and magnetic moments to a high degree of accuracy. These having been established, the technique can now be used to determine the very fine energy shifts which occur within the solid state (such as the interaction between the conduction electrons and nuclei in a metal), or in the structure of a molecule (such as the 'chemical shift' and 'spin–spin coupling' which occur in organic chemistry).

The main reason for including a reference to these two types of spectroscopy in this chapter, however, is that they afford a very good example of the quantized nature of radiation, and of the interaction of these quanta with matter, even at the very low-energy, long-wavelength end of the spectrum.

It will be appreciated that the whole theme of this book has been to try and show how the advent of quantum physics revolutionized our understanding of the nature and properties of radiation as it is found in all the different regions of the spectrum. It has also become clear, however, that in some cases a deeper treatment of the subject is necessary before a complete explanation is to be found. Later texts in this series will in fact follow these points through into a more formal treatment both of wave and quantum mechanics, and of the quantum electrodynamics of radiation itself.

PROBLEMS

6.1. An X-ray tube is operating at 200 kV and with a current of 5 mA. Calculate the shortest wavelength that can be emitted by such a tube. If 0·1 per cent of the energy in the incident electron beam were converted into X-rays at this wavelength, how many quanta per second would be emitted?

6.2. What is the shortest wavelength that can be emitted by the sudden stopping of an electron when it strikes (i) the anode of an X-ray tube operating at 100 kV, (ii) the anode of a high-power transmitting valve operating at 25 kV, and (iii) the screen of a television set operating at 10 kV? Are any of these radiations likely to be harmful?

6.3. Calculate the inherent natural linewidth of a spectral line, which arises from the Uncertainty Principle, if the lifetime of the excited state is (i) 10^{-10} s (ii) 10^{-6} s (iii) 10^{-2} s.

   Compare the approximate resolutions that would then be possible, ignoring all other effects, if the first line was emitted in the γ-ray region and the second in the visible region.

6.4. Over what range of speeds must an ^{57}Fe Mossbauer source be moved if a frequency sweep of 10 MHz about its normal emission frequency is to be obtained? The emission arises from two nuclear energy levels separated by 14·4 keV.

6.5. Calculate the minimum γ-ray energy required to produce (i) an electron–positron pair (ii) a proton–anti-proton pair (iii) an electron–positron pair in which each has a final kinetic energy of 0·5 MeV.

6.6. Calculate the resonance frequency at which a free proton will undergo n.m.r. (i) in a magnetic field of 1 tesla (ii) in the earth's field of 5×10^{-5} tesla.

6.7. The maximum magnetic field produced by the magnetic moment of the copper nucleus at the position of one of its own outer electrons is 1×10^{-2} tesla. What fraction is this of the magnetic field required for electron spin resonance when the applied microwave frequency is 10 000 MHz? If the copper nucleus can have four different quantized orientations in a given field what effect is this interaction likely to have on the observed electron resonance spectra?

6.8. If the γ-ray emitted by the ^{57}Fe nucleus of Problem 6.4. originated from a single atom, rather than from one embedded in a crystal lattice, what would be the change in frequency of the γ-ray?

6.9. Given that a television programme occupies a bandwidth, or frequency-spread, of 5 MHz, calculate the number of independent television programmes that could be transmitted simultaneously down a laser beam which had a spread of wavelengths from 5 000 Å to 6 000 Å.

Index

Physical constants and conversion factors

Avogadro constant L or N_A $6{\cdot}022 \times 10^{23} \text{ mol}^{-1}$
Bohr magneton μ_B $9{\cdot}274 \times 10^{-24} \text{ J T}^{-1}$
Bohr radius a_0 $5{\cdot}292 \times 10^{-11} \text{ m}$
Boltzmann constant k $1{\cdot}381 \times 10^{-23} \text{ J K}^{-1}$

charge of an electron e $-1{\cdot}602 \times 10^{-19} \text{ C}$
Compton wavelength of electron $\lambda_C = h/m_e c = 2{\cdot}426 \times 10^{-12} \text{ m}$
Faraday constant F $9{\cdot}649 \times 10^4 \text{ C mol}^{-1}$
fine structure constant $\alpha = \mu_0 e^2 c/2h = 7{\cdot}297 \times 10^{-3}$ $(\alpha^{-1} = 137{\cdot}0)$

gas constant R $8{\cdot}314 \text{ J K}^{-1} \text{ mol}^{-1}$
gravitational constant G $6{\cdot}673 \times 10^{-11} \text{ N m}^2 \text{ kg}^{-2}$
nuclear magneton μ_N $5{\cdot}051 \times 10^{-27} \text{ J T}^{-1}$
permeability of a vacuum μ_0 $4\pi \times 10^{-7} \text{ H m}^{-1}$ exactly

permittivity of a vacuum ϵ_0 $8{\cdot}854 \times 10^{-12} \text{ F m}^{-1}$ $(1/4\pi\epsilon_0 = 8{\cdot}988 \times 10^9 \text{ m F}^{-1})$
Planck constant h $6{\cdot}626 \times 10^{-34} \text{ J s}$
(Planck constant)/2π $\hbar$ $1{\cdot}055 \times 10^{-34} \text{ J s} = 6{\cdot}582 \times 10^{-16} \text{ eV s}$

rest mass of electron m_e $9{\cdot}110 \times 10^{-31} \text{ kg} = 0{\cdot}511 \text{ MeV}/c^2$
rest mass of proton m_p $1{\cdot}673 \times 10^{-27} \text{ kg} = 938{\cdot}3 \text{ MeV}/c^2$
Rydberg constant $R_\infty = \mu_0^2 m_e e^4 c^3/8h^3 = 1{\cdot}097 \times 10^7 \text{ m}^{-1}$
speed of light in a vacuum c $2{\cdot}998 \times 10^8 \text{ m s}^{-1}$

Stefan–Boltzmann constant $\sigma = 2\pi^5 k^4/15 h^3 c^2 = 5{\cdot}670 \times 10^{-8} \text{ W m}^{-2} \text{ K}^{-4}$
unified atomic mass unit (^{12}C)   u $1{\cdot}661 \times 10^{-27} \text{ kg} = 931{\cdot}5 \text{ MeV}/c^2$
wavelength of a 1 eV photon $1{\cdot}243 \times 10^{-6} \text{ m}$

$1 \text{ Å} = 10^{-10} \text{ m}$; $1 \text{ dyne} = 10^{-5} \text{ N}$; $1 \text{ gauss (G)} = 10^{-4} \text{ tesla (T)}$;
$0°\text{C} = 273{\cdot}15 \text{ K}$; $1 \text{ curie (Ci)} = 3{\cdot}7 \times 10^{10} \text{ s}^{-1}$;
$1 \text{ J} = 10^7 \text{ erg} = 6{\cdot}241 \times 10^{18} \text{ eV}$; $1 \text{ eV} = 1{\cdot}602 \times 10^{-19} \text{ J}$; $1 \text{ cal}_{th} = 4{\cdot}184 \text{ J}$;
$\ln 10 = 2{\cdot}303$; $\ln x = 2{\cdot}303 \log x$; $e = 2{\cdot}718$; $\log e = 0{\cdot}4343$; $\pi = 3{\cdot}142$